JOY TO THE WORLD

FOR THE CHURCH AND SUNDAY SCHOOL

Edited and Compiled by

E. O. EXCELL

Printed in Round and Shaped Notes
with Orchestration

PRICES:

FULL CLOTH, $5.40 the dozen; $45.00 the 100, Not Prepaid
Single Copies, 55 cents, Postpaid
FLEXIBLE MUSLIN, $4.20 the dozen; $35.00 the 100, Not Prepaid
Single Copies, 45 cents, Postpaid

ORCHESTRATION FOR 14 INSTRUMENTS:

1st Violin	2nd Clarinet
2nd Violin	1st and 2nd Cornet
Viola	Flute
Cello	Trombone (Treble Clef)
Bass	Trombone (Bass Clef)
1st Clarinet	Horns (in F)

Twelve Volumes	$15.00
Six Volumes	7.50
Single Copies	1.50

Postage, 10c per copy

HOPE PUBLISHING COMPANY
CHICAGO

FOREWORD

FOR thirty years or more I have compiled and edited music books for Sunday School and Church use, and directed large assemblages in services of song.

The books that bear my name are many. Not a few of them were, and still are, large sellers, but it is my honest opinion that none of my past successes come nearer meeting my high ideal of what a practical all-round and modern music book ought to be than the volume now in your hand. It is my latest and, all things considered, my very best and most satisfactory endeavor.

That "Joy to the World" will have a large and even a phenomenal sale goes without saying. The intrinsic merits of this collection coupled with the resources, originality and resourcefulness of the Hope Publishing Company assure that fact.

JOY TO THE WORLD

No. 1. **Joy to the World.**

Isaac Watts.

G. F. Handel.

1. Joy to the world, the Lord is come! Let earth re - ceive her King; Let ev - 'ry heart pre - pare Him room, And Heav'n and na - ture sing, And Heav'n and na - ture sing, And Heav'n, And Heav'n and na - ture sing.

2. No more let sin and sor - row grow, Nor thorns in - fest the ground; He comes to make His bless - ings flow Far as the curse is found, Far as the curse is found, Far as, Far as the curse is found.

3. He rules the world with truth and grace, And makes the na - tions prove The glo - ries of His right - eous - ness, And won - ders of His love, And won - ders of His love, And won - ders, And won - ders of His love.

(1) And Heav'n and na - ture sing, (And Heav'n and na - ture sing,)

No. 2.   Spend One Hour With Jesus.

WORDS AND MUSIC COPYRIGHT, 1912, BY E. O. EXCELL.
INTERNATIONAL COPYRIGHT SECURED.

Katharine A. Grimes.   E. O. Excell.

1. Wear-y soul by sin op-pressed, Spend one hour with Je-sus;
2. Do you fear the gath-'ring gloom? Spend one hour with Je-sus;
3. Ev-'ry need He will sup-ply, Spend one hour with Je-sus;
4. All a-long life's storm-y way, Spend one hour with Je-sus;

He will give your spir-it rest, Spend one hour with Je-sus:
In the si-lent in-ner room, Spend one hour with Je-sus:
He a-lone can sat-is-fy, Spend one hour with Je-sus:
Call up-on Him day by day, Spend one hour with Je-sus:

He has felt your grief be-fore, Num-bered all your sor-rows o'er,
He will speak un-to your soul, Make your ev-'ry heart-ache whole,
Oh, the mer-cy He will show, Oh, the grace He will be-stow,
Tell Him all— He is your Friend, He will count-less bless-ings send.

He will ev-'ry joy re-store; Spend one hour with Je-sus.
Point you to the Heav'n-ly Goal; Spend one hour with Je-sus.
Grace to con-quer ev-'ry foe; Spend one hour with Je-sus.
He will keep you to the end; Spend one hour with Je-sus.

No. 3.   Jesus, Friend of Sinners.

Charles Irvin Junkin.

Geo. C. Stebbins.

1. Je - sus, Friend of sin - ners, Hast Thou love for me?
2. Je - sus, Friend of sin - ners, Thou hast read my heart,
3. Je - sus, Friend of sin - ners, Thou hast touched my soul,
4. Je - sus, Friend of sin - ners, Bid me fol - low Thee,
5. Je - sus, Friend of sin - ners, Hold me by Thy side,

Son of God the Ho - ly, Man of mys - ter - y,
Searching its re - cess - es, With a lov - er's art;
Not with scorn - ful pit - y, Not with beg - gar's dole;
O'er the rug - ged high - ways, E'en to Cal - va - ry;
Till the shad - ows deep - en Tow'rd the e - ven - tide:

Lov - er of the chil - dren, Teach - er of the wise,
Naught have I with - hold - en, Noth - ing hid from Thee,
Thou hast not de - spis - ed Men that faint or fall,
Let me know Thy Spir - it, Sweet and strong and wise;
To Thy strength and beau - ty I would ev - er bend,

Let me read the se - cret In Thy friend - ly eyes.
Waste, or want, or fol - ly, Things that should not be.
Ten - der - er than broth - er, For Thou know - est all.
I would win the friend - ship In Thy lov - ing eyes.
Till, in dawn e - ter - nal, Friend shall be as friend!

No. 4. I've Found a Friend.

J. G. Small.

Geo. C. Stebbins.

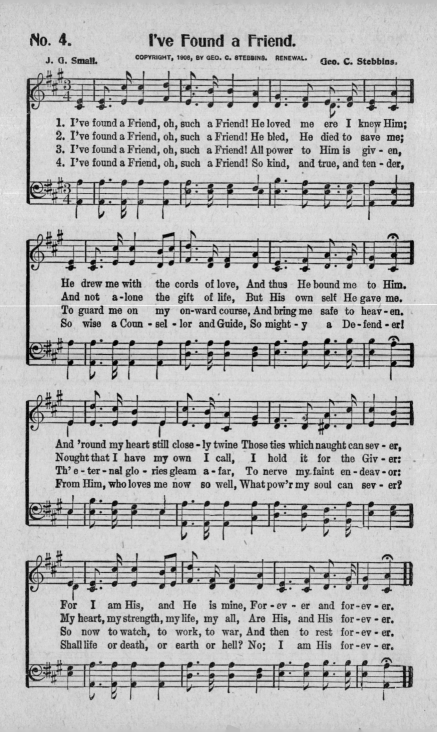

1. I've found a Friend, oh, such a Friend! He loved me ere I knew Him;
2. I've found a Friend, oh, such a Friend! He bled, He died to save me;
3. I've found a Friend, oh, such a Friend! All power to Him is giv-en,
4. I've found a Friend, oh, such a Friend! So kind, and true, and ten-der,

He drew me with the cords of love, And thus He bound me to Him.
And not a-lone the gift of life, But His own self He gave me.
To guard me on my on-ward course, And bring me safe to heav-en.
So wise a Coun-sel-lor and Guide, So might-y a De-fend-er!

And 'round my heart still close-ly twine Those ties which naught can sev-er,
Nought that I have my own I call, I hold it for the Giv-er:
Th' e-ter-nal glo-ries gleam a-far, To nerve my faint en-deav-or:
From Him, who loves me now so well, What pow'r my soul can sev-er?

For I am His, and He is mine, For-ev-er and for-ev-er.
My heart, my strength, my life, my all, Are His, and His for-ev-er.
So now to watch, to work, to war, And then to rest for-ev-er.
Shall life or death, or earth or hell? No; I am His for-ev-er.

Jesus is All the World to Me.

W. L. T.

Will L. Thompson.

1. Je - sus is all the world to me, My life, my joy, my all;
2. Je - sus is all the world to me, My Friend in tri - als sore;
3. Je - sus is all the world to me, And true to Him I'll be;
4. Je - sus is all the world to me, I want no bet - ter friend;

He is my strength from day to day, With-out Him I would fall.
I go to Him for bless-ings, and He gives them o'er and o'er.
Oh, how could I this Friend de - ny, When He's so true to me?
I trust Him now, I'll trust Him when Life's fleet-ing days shall end.

When I am sad, to Him I go, No oth - er one can
He sends the sun - shine and the rain, He sends the har - vest's
Fol - low - ing Him I know I'm right, He watch - es o'er me
Beau - ti - ful life with such a Friend; Beau - ti - ful life that

cheer me so; When I am sad He makes me glad, He's my Friend.
gold - en grain; Sun-shine and rain, har - vest of grain, He's my Friend.
day and night; Fol-low-ing Him, by day and night, He's my Friend.
has no end; E - ter - nal life, e - ter - nal joy, He's my Friend.

No. 6.　　　　Jesus Saves.

Priscilla J. Owens.　　COPYRIGHT, 1910, BY WM. J. KIRKPATRICK, IN RENEWAL.　　Wm. J. Kirkpatrick.

1. We have heard the joy-ful sound: Je - sus saves! Je - sus saves!
2. Waft it on the roll - ing tide; Je - sus saves! Je - sus saves!
3. Sing a - bove the bat - tle strife, Je - sus saves! Je - sus saves!
4. Give the winds a might-y voice, Je - sus saves! Je - sus saves!

Spread the ti - dings all a - round: Je - sus saves! Je - sus saves!
Tell to sin - ners far and wide: Je - sus saves! Je - sus saves!
By His death and end - less life, Je - sus saves! Je - sus saves!
Let the na - tions now re - joice,—Je - sus saves! Je - sus saves!

Bear the news to ev - 'ry land, Climb the steeps and cross the waves;
Sing, ye is - lands of the sea; Ech - o back, ye o - cean caves;
Sing it soft - ly thro' the gloom, When the heart for mer - cy craves;
Shout sal - va - tion full and free, High - est hills and deep - est caves;

On - ward!—'tis our Lord's com-mand; Je - sus saves! Je - sus saves!
Earth shall keep her ju - bi - lee: Je - sus saves! Je - sus saves!
Sing in tri - umph o'er the tomb,—Je - sus saves! Je - sus saves!
This our song of vic - to - ry,— Je - sus saves! Je - sus saves!

No. 7.   Jesus, Blessed Jesus.

C. H. G.

Chas. H. Gabriel.

1. There's One who can comfort when all else fails, Je - sus, bless-ed Je - sus;
2. He hear-eth the cry of the soul distressed, Je - sus, bless-ed Je - sus;
3. He nev - er for-sakes in the dark-est hour, Je - sus, bless-ed Je - sus;
4. What joy it will be when we see His face, Je - sus, bless-ed Je - sus;

A Sav - ior who saves tho' the foe as-sails, Je - sus, bless-ed Je - sus:
He heal-eth the wounded, He giv-eth rest, Je - sus, bless-ed Je - sus:
His arm is a-round us with keep-ing pow'r, Je - sus, bless-ed Je - sus:
For - ev - er to sing of His love and grace, Je - sus, bless-ed Je - sus:

Once He trav-eled the way we go, Felt the pangs of de - ceit and woe;
When from loved ones we're called to part, When the tears in our an-guish start,
When we en - ter the Shad-ow-land, When at Jor - dan we trembling stand,
There at home on that shin - ing shore, With the loved ones gone on be - fore,

Who more per - fect-ly then can know, Than Je - sus, bless-ed Je - sus?
None can com - fort the break-ing heart Like Je - sus, bless-ed Je - sus.
He will meet us with outstretched hand, This Je - sus, bless-ed Je - sus.
We will praise Him for - ev - er-more, Our Je - sus, bless-ed Je - sus.

No. 8. He Supplieth All of My Need.

T. O. Chisholm.

Chas. H. Gabriel.

1. All of my need He free-ly sup-pli-eth, Day aft-er day His good-ness I prove; Mer-cies un-fail-ing, new ev-'ry morn-ing, Tell me of God's un-change-a-ble love.

2. All of my need He free-ly sup-pli-eth, Wis-dom and guid-ance, strength as my day; Grace for each tri-al, com-fort in sor-row, Bless-ed com-mun-ion all of the way.

3. All of my need He free-ly sup-pli-eth, There's not a void that He can-not feel; Nev-er a bur-den He can-not light-en, Nev-er a heart-ache He can-not heal.

4. All of my need He free-ly sup-pli-eth, I shall not want, what-ev-er be-tide; He that de-liv-ered Christ for my ran-som, With Him will all things sure-ly pro-vide.

FINE.

CHORUS.

God hath laid help on One that is might-y, One who is Friend and Broth-er in-deed;

D. S.—Noth-ing have I, yet I am con-tent-ed, For He sup-pli-eth all of my need.

D. S.

No. 9. 'Tis the Blessed Hour of Prayer.

Fanny J. Crosby.

W. H. Doane.

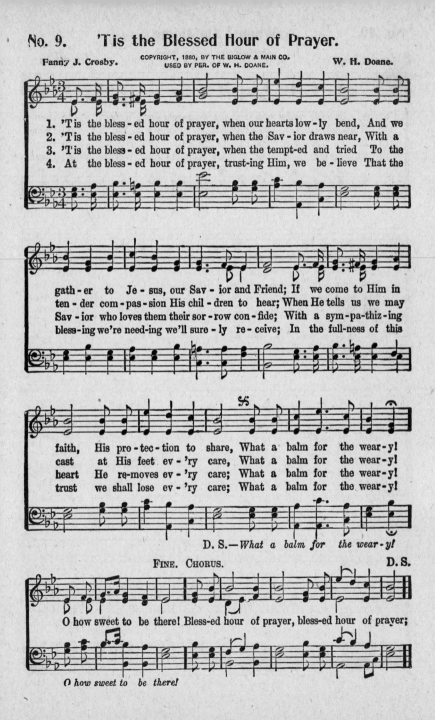

1. 'Tis the bless-ed hour of prayer, when our hearts low-ly bend, And we
2. 'Tis the bless-ed hour of prayer, when the Sav-ior draws near, With a
3. 'Tis the bless-ed hour of prayer, when the tempt-ed and tried To the
4. At the bless-ed hour of prayer, trust-ing Him, we be-lieve That the

gath-er to Je-sus, our Sav-ior and Friend; If we come to Him in
ten-der com-pas-sion His chil-dren to hear; When He tells us we may
Sav-ior who loves them their sor-row con-fide; With a sym-pa-thiz-ing
bless-ing we're need-ing we'll sure-ly re-ceive; In the full-ness of this

faith, His pro-tec-tion to share, What a balm for the wear-y!
cast at His feet ev-'ry care, What a balm for the wear-y!
heart He re-moves ev-'ry care; What a balm for the wear-y!
trust we shall lose ev-'ry care; What a balm for the wear-y!

D. S.—*What a balm for the wear-y!*

FINE. CHORUS.   D. S.

O how sweet to be there! Bless-ed hour of prayer, bless-ed hour of prayer;

O how sweet to be there!

No. 10.

When I Go Home.

Jennie Ree.　　　　　　　　　　　　　　　　　　　Chas. H. Gabriel.

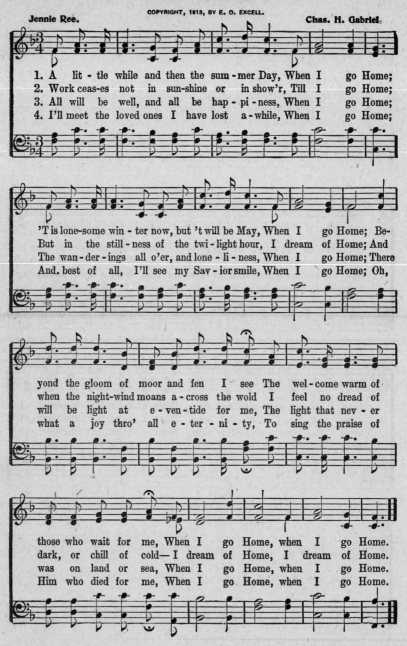

1. A lit - tle while and then the sum - mer Day, When I go Home;
2. Work ceas-es not in sun-shine or in show'r, Till I go Home;
3. All will be well, and all be hap - pi - ness, When I go Home;
4. I'll meet the loved ones I have lost a - while, When I go Home;

'T is lone-some win - ter now, but 't will be May, When I go Home; Be-
But in the still - ness of the twi - light hour, I dream of Home; And
The wan - der - ings all o'er, and lone - li - ness, When I go Home; There
And, best of all, I'll see my Sav - ior smile, When I go Home; Oh,

yond the gloom of moor and fen I see The wel - come warm of
when the night-wind moans a - cross the wold I feel no dread of
will be light at e - ven-tide for me, The light that nev - er
what a joy thro' all e - ter - ni - ty, To sing the praise of

those who wait for me, When I go Home, when I go Home.
dark, or chill of cold— I dream of Home, I dream of Home.
was on land or sea, When I go Home, when I go Home.
Him who died for me, When I go Home, when I go Home.

No. 11. Crown Him With Many Crowns.

Matthew Bridges.

George J. Elvey.

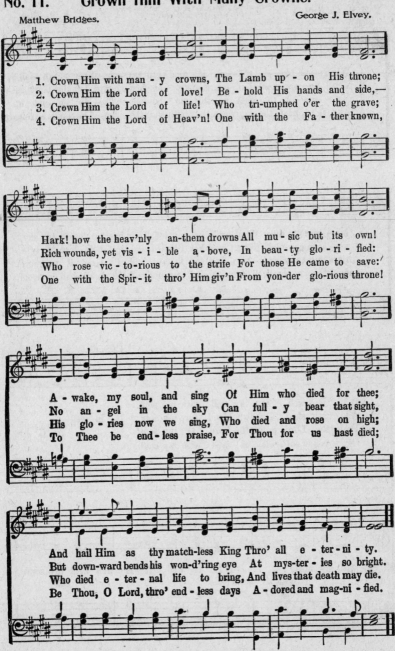

1. Crown Him with man - y crowns, The Lamb up - on His throne;
2. Crown Him the Lord of love! Be - hold His hands and side,—
3. Crown Him the Lord of life! Who tri - umphed o'er the grave;
4. Crown Him the Lord of Heav'n! One with the Fa - ther known,

Hark! how the heav'nly an-them drowns All mu - sic but its own!
Rich wounds, yet vis - i - ble a - bove, In beau - ty glo - ri - fied:
Who rose vic - to - rious to the strife For those He came to save:
One with the Spir - it thro' Him giv'n From yon - der glo - rious throne!

A - wake, my soul, and sing Of Him who died for thee;
No an - gel in the sky Can full - y bear that sight,
His glo - ries now we sing, Who died and rose on high;
To Thee be end - less praise, For Thou for us hast died;

And hail Him as thy match-less King Thro' all e - ter - ni - ty.
But down-ward bends his won-d'ring eye At mys - ter - ies so bright.
Who died e - ter - nal life to bring, And lives that death may die.
Be Thou, O Lord, thro' end - less days A - dored and mag - ni - fied.

No. 12. It Is Well With My Soul.

H. G. Spafford. COPYRIGHT, 1904, BY THE JOHN CHURCH CO. USED BY PERMISSION. P. P. Bliss.

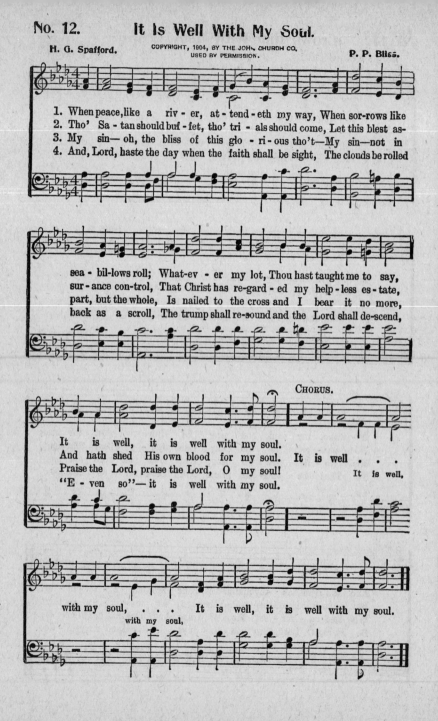

1. When peace, like a riv-er, at-tend-eth my way, When sor-rows like sea-bil-lows roll; What-ev-er my lot, Thou hast taught me to say,
2. Tho' Sa-tan should buf-fet, tho' tri-als should come, Let this blest as-sur-ance con-trol, That Christ has re-gard-ed my help-less es-tate,
3. My sin— oh, the bliss of this glo-ri-ous tho't—My sin—not in part, but the whole, Is nailed to the cross and I bear it no more,
4. And, Lord, haste the day when the faith shall be sight, The clouds be rolled back as a scroll, The trump shall re-sound and the Lord shall de-scend,

CHORUS.

It is well, it is well with my soul.
And hath shed His own blood for my soul.
Praise the Lord, praise the Lord, O my soul!
"E-ven so"— it is well with my soul.

It is well . . . with my soul, . . . It is well, it is well with my soul.

It is well, with my soul,

No. 13.   Let Him In.

Rev. J. B. Atchinson.

E. O. Excell.

1. There's a Stran-ger at the door,   Let   Him in;
2. O - pen now to Him your heart,   Let   Him in;
3. Hear you now His lov-ing voice?   Let   Him in;
4. Now ad-mit the heav'n-ly Guest,   Let   Him in;

Let the Sav-ior in,   Let the Sav-ior in;

He has been there oft be-fore,   Let   Him in;
If you wait He will de-part,   Let   Him in;
Now, oh, now make Him your choice,   Let   Him in;
He will make for you a feast,   Let   Him in;

Let the Sav-ior in,   Let the Sav-ior in;

Let Him in, ere He is gone, Let Him in, the Ho-ly One,
Let Him in, He is your Friend, He your soul will sure de-fend,
He is stand-ing at your door, Joy to you He will re-store,
He will speak your sins for-giv'n, And when earth-ties all are riv'n,

Je-sus Christ, the Fa-ther's Son,   Let   Him in.
He will keep you to the end,   Let   Him in.
And His name you will a-dore,   Let   Him in.
He will take you home to heav'n,   Let   Him in.

Let the Sav-ior in,   Let the Sav-ior in.

No. 14.

I Must Tell Jesus.

E. A. H.

COPYRIGHT, 1893, BY THE HOFFMAN MUSIC CO.

Rev. E. A. Hoffman.

1. I must tell Je - sus all of my tri - als; I can - not bear these
2. I must tell Jo - sus all of my troub - les; He is a kind, com -
3. Tempted and tried I need a great Sav - ior, One who can help my
4. O how the world to e - vil al - lures me! O how my heart is

bur - dens a - lone; In my dis - tress He kind - ly will help me;
pas - sion - ate Friend; If I but ask Him, He will de - liv - er,
bur - dens to bear; I must tell Je - sus, I must tell Je - sus;
tempted to sin! I must tell Je - sus, and He will help me

D. S.—*I must tell Je - sus! I must tell Je - sus!*

FINE. CHORUS.

He ev - er loves and cares for His own.
Make of my troub - les quick - ly an end.   I must tell Je - sus!
He all my cares and sor - rows will share.
O - ver the world the vic - t'ry to win.

Je - sus can help me, Je - sus a - lone.

D. S.

I must tell Je - sus! I can - not bear my bur - dens a - lone;

No. 15.   As a Volunteer.

W. S. Brown.   Chas. H. Gabriel.

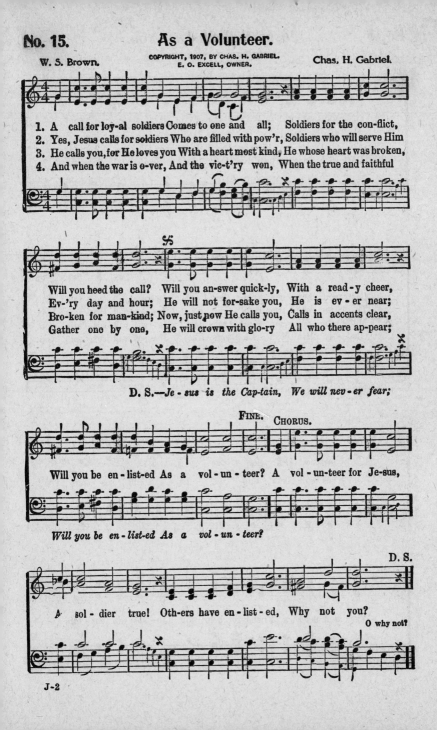

1. A call for loy-al soldiers Comes to one and all;   Soldiers for the con-flict,
2. Yes, Jesus calls for soldiers Who are filled with pow'r, Soldiers who will serve Him
3. He calls you, for He loves you With a heart most kind, He whose heart was broken,
4. And when the war is o-ver, And the vic-t'ry won, When the true and faithful

Will you heed the call? Will you an-swer quick-ly, With a read-y cheer,
Ev-'ry day and hour; He will not for-sake you, He is ev-er near;
Bro-ken for man-kind; Now, just now He calls you, Calls in accents clear,
Gather one by one, He will crown with glo-ry All who there ap-pear;

D. S.—Je-sus is the Cap-tain, We will nev-er fear;

FINE. CHORUS.

Will you be en-list-ed As a vol-un-teer? A vol-un-teer for Je-sus,
Will you be en-list-ed As a vol-un-teer?

D. S.

A sol-dier true! Oth-ers have en-list-ed, Why not you?
O why not?

J-2

No. 16.   Jesus Will Sustain You.

James Rowe.

B. D. Ackley.

1. Does the world no rest af-ford? Would you have your strength re-stored?
2. Are you tempt-ed by the foe? Has your bur-den laid you low?
3. Are you wear-y of the fray? Have you fall-en by the way?
4. Dark with sin your past may be, Je-sus waits to hear your plea,

Cast your bur-den on the Lord, Je-sus will sus-tain you.
To the one true Help-er go, Je-sus will sus-tain you.
Make the Sav-ior yours to-day, Je-sus will sus-tain you.
Glad-ly He will set you free; Je-sus will sus-tain you.

CHORUS.

Je-sus will sus-tain you, Je-sus will sus-tain you;

When you need a Friend to help you, Je-sus will sus-tain you.

No. 17.   Take the Name of Jesus With You.

Mrs. Lydia Baxter.   W. H. Doane.

1. Take the name of Je - sus with you, Child of sor-row and of woe;
2. Take the name of Je - sus ev - er As a shield from ev-'ry snare;
3. O   the precious name of Je - sus! How it thrills our souls with joy,
4. At the name of Je - sus bow - ing, Fall-ing prostrate at His feet,

It   will joy and com-fort give you, Take it then, where'er you go.
If   temp - ta - tions round you gath - er, Breathe that ho - ly name in prayer.
When His lov - ing arms re-ceive us, And His songs our tongues em-ploy!
King of kings in Heav'n we'll crown Him, When our jour-ney is com-plete.

CHORUS.

Precious name,   O how sweet!   Hope of earth and joy of Heav'n;
Precious name,   O how sweet!

Precious name,   O how sweet!   Hope of earth and joy of Heav'n.
Precious name, O how sweet, how sweet!

No. 18.   The Touch of His Hand on Mine.

Jessie Brown Pounds.

Henry P. Morton.

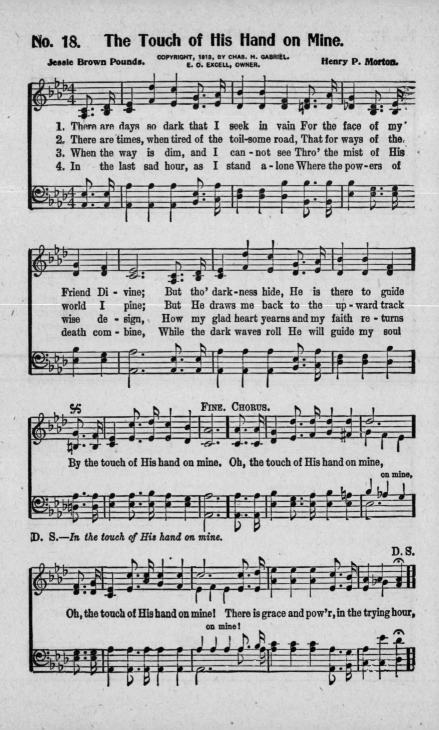

1. There are days so dark that I seek in vain For the face of my Friend Di - vine; But tho' dark-ness hide, He is there to guide
2. There are times, when tired of the toil-some road, That for ways of the world I pine; But He draws me back to the up - ward track
3. When the way is dim, and I can - not see Thro' the mist of His wise de - sign, How my glad heart yearns and my faith re - turns
4. In the last sad hour, as I stand a - lone Where the pow-ers of death com - bine, While the dark waves roll He will guide my soul

FINE. CHORUS.

By the touch of His hand on mine. Oh, the touch of His hand on mine,
on mine,

D. S.—*In the touch of His hand on mine.*

D. S.

Oh, the touch of His hand on mine! There is grace and pow'r, in the trying hour,
on mine!

No. 19. The Gifts of God.

Jessie Brown Pounds.

E. O. Excell.

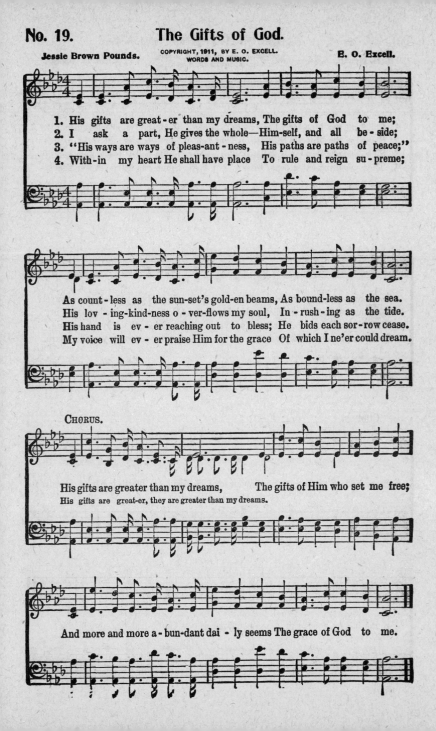

1. His gifts are great-er than my dreams, The gifts of God to me;
2. I ask a part, He gives the whole—Him-self, and all be-side;
3. "His ways are ways of pleas-ant-ness, His paths are paths of peace;"
4. With-in my heart He shall have place To rule and reign su-preme;

As count-less as the sun-set's gold-en beams, As bound-less as the sea.
His lov-ing-kind-ness o-ver-flows my soul, In-rush-ing as the tide.
His hand is ev-er reaching out to bless; He bids each sor-row cease.
My voice will ev-er praise Him for the grace Of which I ne'er could dream.

CHORUS.

His gifts are greater than my dreams, The gifts of Him who set me free;
His gifts are great-er, they are greater than my dreams.

And more and more a-bun-dant dai-ly seems The grace of God to me.

No. 20. Somebody Needs You.

E. E. Hewitt.

Chas. H. Gabriel.

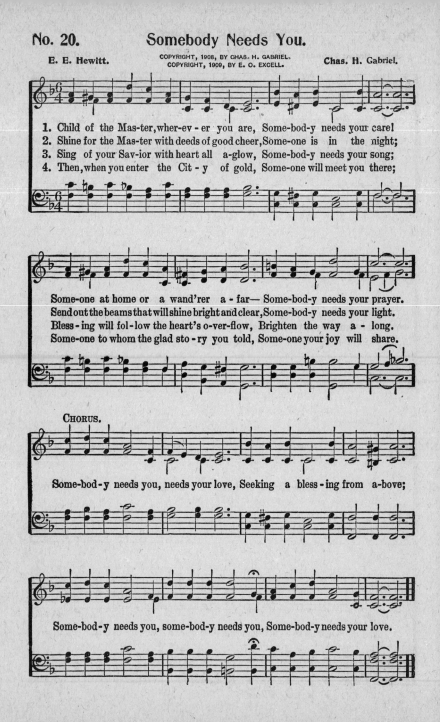

1. Child of the Mas-ter, wher-ev-er you are, Some-bod-y needs your care!
2. Shine for the Mas-ter with deeds of good cheer, Some-one is in the night;
3. Sing of your Sav-ior with heart all a-glow, Some-bod-y needs your song;
4. Then, when you enter the Cit-y of gold, Some-one will meet you there;

Some-one at home or a wand'rer a-far— Some-bod-y needs your prayer.
Send out the beams that will shine bright and clear, Some-bod-y needs your light.
Bless-ing will fol-low the heart's o-ver-flow, Brighten the way a-long.
Some-one to whom the glad sto-ry you told, Some-one your joy will share.

CHORUS.

Some-bod-y needs you, needs your love, Seeking a bless-ing from a-bove;

Some-bod-y needs you, some-bod-y needs you, Some-bod-y needs your love.

No. 21. I Would Be Like Jesus.

James Rowe.

B. D. Ackley.

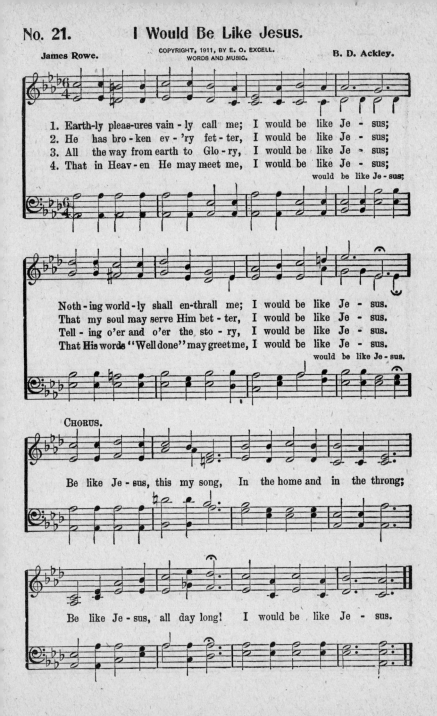

1. Earth-ly pleas-ures vain - ly call me; I would be like Je - sus;
2. He has bro - ken ev - 'ry fet - ter, I would be like Je - sus;
3. All the way from earth to Glo - ry, I would be like Je - sus;
4. That in Heav - en He may meet me, I would be like Je - sus;

would be like Je - sus;

Noth - ing world - ly shall en-thrall me; I would be like Je - sus.
That my soul may serve Him bet - ter, I would be like Je - sus.
Tell - ing o'er and o'er the sto - ry, I would be like Je - sus.
That His words "Well done" may greet me, I would be like Je - sus.

would be like Je - sus.

Chorus.

Be like Je - sus, this my song, In the home and in the throng;

Be like Je - sus, all day long! I would be like Je - sus.

No. 22. Just When I Need Him Most.

Rev. Wm. Pool.

Chas. H. Gabriel.

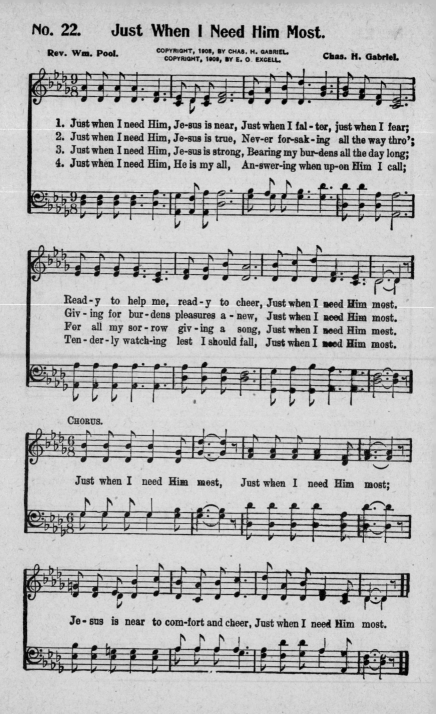

1. Just when I need Him, Je-sus is near, Just when I fal - ter, just when I fear;
2. Just when I need Him, Je-sus is true, Nev-er for-sak-ing all the way thro';
3. Just when I need Him, Je-sus is strong, Bearing my bur-dens all the day long;
4. Just when I need Him, He is my all, An-swer-ing when up-on Him I call;

Read-y to help me, read-y to cheer, Just when I need Him most.
Giv-ing for bur-dens pleasures a - new, Just when I need Him most.
For all my sor-row giv-ing a song, Just when I need Him most.
Ten-der-ly watch-ing lest I should fall, Just when I need Him most.

CHORUS.

Just when I need Him most, Just when I need Him most;

Je-sus is near to com-fort and cheer, Just when I need Him most.

No. 23. Grace, Enough for Me.

B. O. E.

WORDS AND MUSIC COPYRIGHT, 1905, BY E. O. EXCELL.
INTERNATIONAL COPYRIGHT SECURED.

E. O. Excell.

1. In look-ing thro' my tears one day, I saw Mount Cal-va-ry;
2. While standing there, my trembling heart, Once full of ag-o-ny,
3. When I be-held my ev-'ry sin Nailed to the cru-el tree,
4. When I am safe with-in the veil, My por-tion there will be,

Beneath the cross there flowed a stream Of grace, e-nough for me.
Could scarce believe the sight I saw Of grace, e-nough for me. (enough for me.)
I felt a flood go thro' my soul Of grace, e-nough for me.
To sing thro' all the years to come Of grace, e-nough for me.

CHORUS.

Grace is flowing from Calvary, . . Grace as fathomless as the sea, . .
Grace is flow-ing from Cal-va-ry for me, Grace as fath-om-less as the roll-ing sea,

Grace for time and e-ter-ni-ty, . . . Grace, . . enough for me.
Grace for time and e-ter-ni-ty, His a-bun-dant grace I see, e-nough for me.

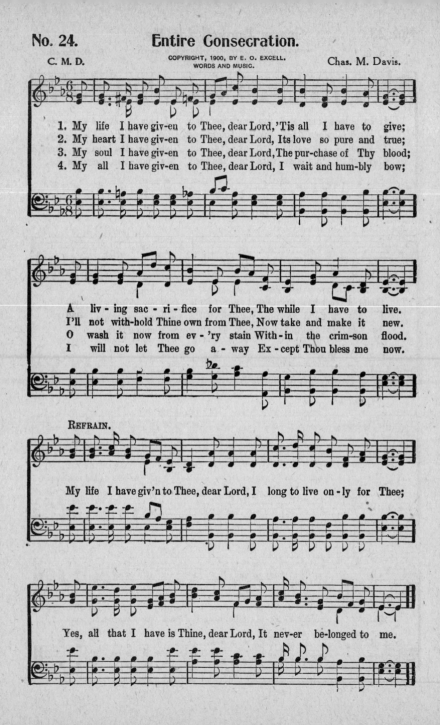

No. 24.   Entire Consecration.

C. M. D.

COPYRIGHT, 1900, BY E. O. EXCELL.
WORDS AND MUSIC.

Chas. M. Davis.

1. My life I have giv-en to Thee, dear Lord, 'Tis all I have to give;
2. My heart I have giv-en to Thee, dear Lord, Its love so pure and true;
3. My soul I have giv-en to Thee, dear Lord, The pur-chase of Thy blood;
4. My all I have giv-en to Thee, dear Lord, I wait and hum-bly bow;

A liv-ing sac-ri-fice for Thee, The while I have to live.
I'll not with-hold Thine own from Thee, Now take and make it new.
O wash it now from ev-'ry stain With-in the crim-son flood.
I will not let Thee go a-way Ex-cept Thou bless me now.

REFRAIN.

My life I have giv'n to Thee, dear Lord, I long to live on-ly for Thee;

Yes, all that I have is Thine, dear Lord, It nev-er be-longed to me.

No. 25.   Sweeter Than All.

Rev. Johnson Oatman, Jr.

J. Howard Entwisle.

1. Christ will me His aid af-ford, Nev-er to fall, nev-er to fall;
2. I can fol-low all the way, Hear-ing Him call, hear-ing Him call;
3. Tho' a ves-sel I may be, Bro-ken and small, bro-ken and small,
4. When I reach the crys-tal sea, Voi-ces will call, voi-ces will call;

While I find my pre-cious Lord Sweet-er than all, sweet-er than all.
Find-ing Him, from day to day, Sweet-er than all, sweet-er than all.
Yet His bless-ings fall on me, Sweet-er than all, sweet-er than all.
But my Sav-ior's voice will be Sweet-er than all, sweet-er than all.

CHORUS.

Je-sus is now and ev-er will be, Sweet-er than all the world to me,

Since I heard His lov-ing call, Sweet-er than all, sweet-er than all.

No. 26. Bring Peace to My Soul.

Helen M. Dungan.

J. M. Dungan.

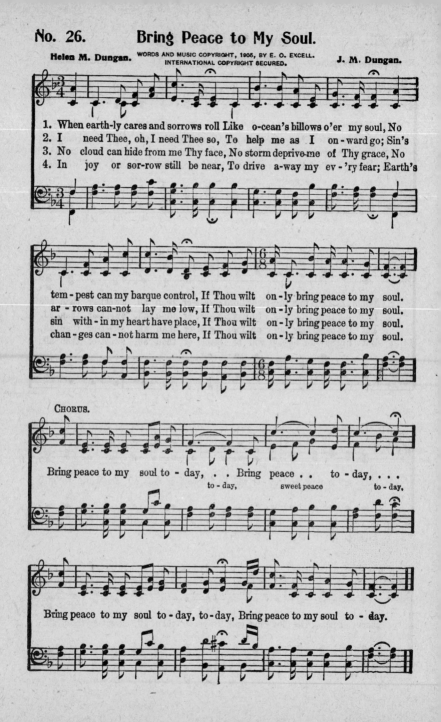

1. When earth-ly cares and sorrows roll Like o-cean's billows o'er my soul, No
2. I need Thee, oh, I need Thee so, To help me as I on-ward go; Sin's
3. No cloud can hide from me Thy face, No storm deprive me of Thy grace, No
4. In joy or sor-row still be near, To drive a-way my ev-'ry fear; Earth's

tem-pest can my barque control, If Thou wilt on-ly bring peace to my soul.
ar-rows can-not lay me low, If Thou wilt on-ly bring peace to my soul.
sin with-in my heart have place, If Thou wilt on-ly bring peace to my soul.
chan-ges can-not harm me here, If Thou wilt on-ly bring peace to my soul.

CHORUS.

Bring peace to my soul to-day, . . Bring peace . . to-day, . . .
to-day, sweet peace to-day.

Bring peace to my soul to-day, to-day, Bring peace to my soul to-day.

Come to the Feast.

Charlotte G. Homer.

W. A. Ogden.

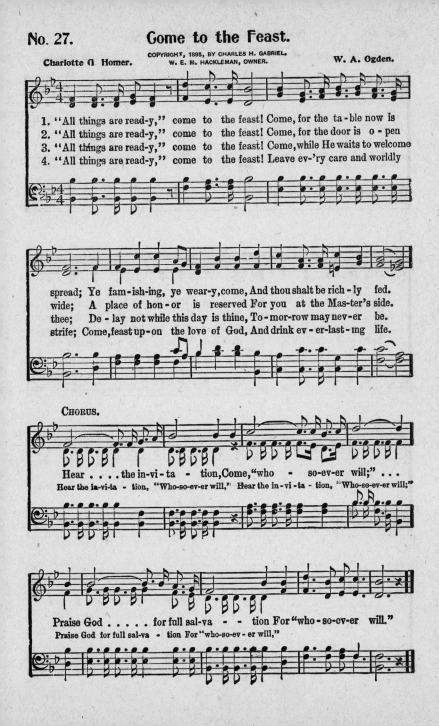

1. "All things are read-y," come to the feast! Come, for the ta-ble now is
2. "All things are read-y," come to the feast! Come, for the door is o-pen
3. "All things are read-y," come to the feast! Come, while He waits to welcome
4. "All things are read-y," come to the feast! Leave ev-'ry care and worldly

spread; Ye fam-ish-ing, ye wear-y, come, And thou shalt be rich-ly fed.
wide; A place of hon-or is reserved For you at the Mas-ter's side.
thee; De-lay not while this day is thine, To-mor-row may nev-er be.
strife; Come, feast up-on the love of God, And drink ev-er-last-ing life.

CHORUS.

Hear .... the in-vi-ta - tion, Come, "who - so-ev-er will;" ...
Hear the in-vi-ta - tion, "Who-so-ev-er will," Hear the in-vi-ta - tion, "Who-so-ev-er will;"

Praise God ..... for full sal-va - - tion For "who-so-ev-er will."
Praise God for full sal-va - tion For "who-so-ev-er will,"

Save One Soul for Jesus.

Rev. Elisha A. Hoffman.

Charlie D. Tillman.

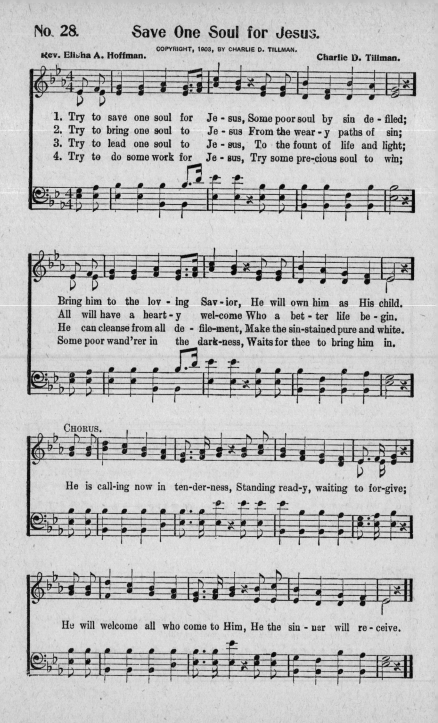

1. Try to save one soul for Je-sus, Some poor soul by sin de-filed;
2. Try to bring one soul to Je-sus From the wear-y paths of sin;
3. Try to lead one soul to Je-sus, To the fount of life and light;
4. Try to do some work for Je-sus, Try some pre-cious soul to win;

Bring him to the lov-ing Sav-ior, He will own him as His child.
All will have a heart-y wel-come Who a bet-ter life be-gin.
He can cleanse from all de-file-ment, Make the sin-stained pure and white.
Some poor wand'rer in the dark-ness, Waits for thee to bring him in.

CHORUS.

He is call-ing now in ten-der-ness, Standing read-y, waiting to for-give;

He will welcome all who come to Him, He the sin-ner will re-ceive.

I am Thine, O Lord.

F. J. Crosby.

W. H. Doane.

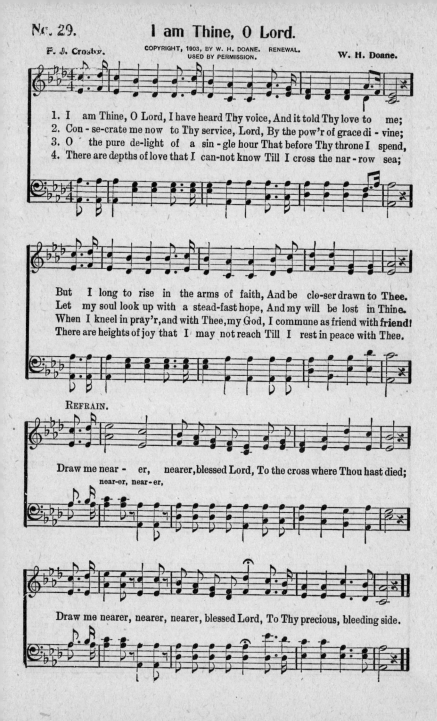

1. I am Thine, O Lord, I have heard Thy voice, And it told Thy love to me;
2. Con - se-crate me now to Thy service, Lord, By the pow'r of grace di - vine;
3. O the pure de-light of a sin - gle hour That before Thy throne I spend,
4. There are depths of love that I can-not know Till I cross the nar - row sea;

But I long to rise in the arms of faith, And be clo-ser drawn to Thee.
Let my soul look up with a stead-fast hope, And my will be lost in Thine.
When I kneel in pray'r, and with Thee, my God, I commune as friend with friend!
There are heights of joy that I may not reach Till I rest in peace with Thee.

REFRAIN.

Draw me near - er, nearer, blessed Lord, To the cross where Thou hast died;

near-er, near-er,

Draw me nearer, nearer, nearer, blessed Lord, To Thy precious, bleeding side.

Teach Me.

COPYRIGHT, 1903, BY E. O. EXCELL.
WORDS AND MUSIC.

Kate Ulmer. Victor H. Benke.

1. Teach me, O, Thou Ho-ly Spir-it, How to do my Master's will;
2. Teach me how to be sub-miss-ive, Free-ly con-se-crat-ing all;
3. Teach me how to trust Him full-y, E'en when faith is sore-ly tried;
4. Teach me how to fol-low tru-ly, Nev-er run-ning on be-fore;

In o-be-dience to His bid-ding, Help me His commands ful-fill.
Fond-est hopes with joy re-sign-ing, In sur-ren-der to His call.
Teach me how to tell the sto-ry Of a Sav-ior cru-ci-fied.
Ev-er in His foot-steps walk-ing, Till my serv-ice here is o'er.

CHORUS.

Teach me, teach me, Teach me ev'ry day what to do and what to say;
Teach me, Ho-ly Spir-it, teach me, Ho-ly Spir-it,

Teach me, teach me How to do my Master's will.
Teach me, Ho-ly Spir-it, teach me, Ho-ly Spir-it, my Master's will.

One Day for Thee.

Rev. W. C. Pool.

Chas. H. Gabriel.

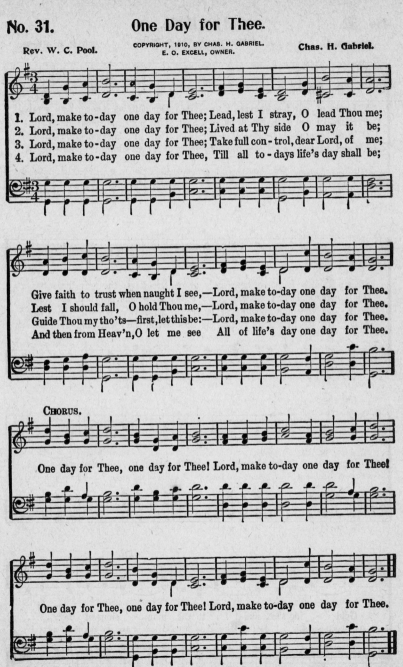

1. Lord, make to-day one day for Thee; Lead, lest I stray, O lead Thou me;
2. Lord, make to-day one day for Thee; Lived at Thy side O may it be;
3. Lord, make to-day one day for Thee; Take full con-trol, dear Lord, of me;
4. Lord, make to-day one day for Thee, Till all to-days life's day shall be;

Give faith to trust when naught I see,—Lord, make to-day one day for Thee.
Lest I should fall, O hold Thou me,—Lord, make to-day one day for Thee.
Guide Thou my tho'ts—first, let this be:—Lord, make to-day one day for Thee.
And then from Heav'n, O let me see All of life's day one day for Thee.

CHORUS.

One day for Thee, one day for Thee! Lord, make to-day one day for Thee!

One day for Thee, one day for Thee! Lord, make to-day one day for Thee.

No. 32. The Bible.

COPYRIGHT, 1887, BY E. O. EXCELL.
WORDS AND MUSIC.

B. Barton.

E. O. Excell.

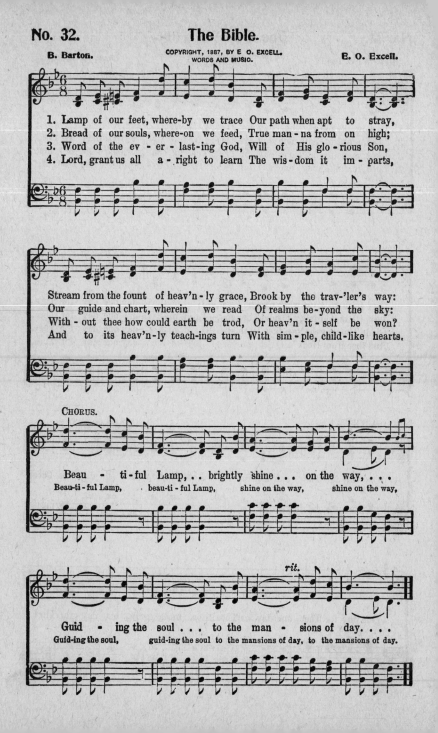

1. Lamp of our feet, where-by we trace Our path when apt to stray,
2. Bread of our souls, where-on we feed, True man-na from on high;
3. Word of the ev-er-last-ing God, Will of His glo-rious Son,
4. Lord, grant us all a-right to learn The wis-dom it im-parts,

Stream from the fount of heav'n-ly grace, Brook by the trav-'ler's way:
Our guide and chart, wherein we read Of realms be-yond the sky:
With-out thee how could earth be trod, Or heav'n it-self be won?
And to its heav'n-ly teach-ings turn With sim-ple, child-like hearts.

CHORUS.

Beau - ti-ful Lamp, .. brightly shine ... on the way, ...
Beau-ti-ful Lamp, beau-ti-ful Lamp, shine on the way, shine on the way,

rit.

Guid - ing the soul ... to the man - sions of day. ...
Guid-ing the soul, guid-ing the soul to the mansions of day, to the mansions of day.

No. 33. The Hour of Prayer.

Fanny J. Crosby.

Jno. R. Sweney.

1. Glo-ry to God for the joy to meet, Here at the hour of prayer;
2. Far from the world we may turn a-way, Here at the hour of prayer;
3. Rich are the blessings that all may seek, Here at the hour of prayer;
4. O what a ho-ly and calm re-pose, Here at the hour of prayer;

Welcome the bliss of com-mun-ion sweet, Here at the hour of prayer.
Glad-ly we rest from the toils of day, Here at the hour of prayer.
Grace for the wear-y, the faint, the weak, Here at the hour of prayer.
Love in its full-ness the heart o'er-flows, Here at the hour of prayer.

CHORUS.

Nearer the gate to the soul's bright home, Nearer the vales where the faithful roam,

Near-er to God and the Lamb we come, Here at the hour of prayer,

Where Thou Callest Me.

James Apple.

Jno. R. Sweney.

1. O how pre-cious are the mo-ments Of com-mun-ing, Lord, with Thee,
2. When the morn, with ro-sy fin - gers, O-pens wide the gates of day,
3. In the se - cret of Thy pres-ence, O - ver-shad-owed with Thy love,
4. In the se - cret of Thy pres-ence, Where, for-get-ting ev - 'ry care,

In the se - cret of Thy presence, Where my soul de-lights to be!
And the mist up - on the moun-tain In - to sun-shine fades a - way,—
Where the peace that passeth knowledge Floweth gen - tly from a - bove,
I may come to Thee still clo - ser On the wings of faith and prayer.

CHORUS.

Sav - ior mine,.... O Sav-ior mine,.... I would ev - er, I would ev-er be
Precious Savior mine, O precious Savior mine,

In the se - cret of Thy presence, Where Thou callest, where Thou callest me!

No. 35. Help Somebody To-day.

Mrs. Frank A. Breck.

Chas. H. Gabriel.

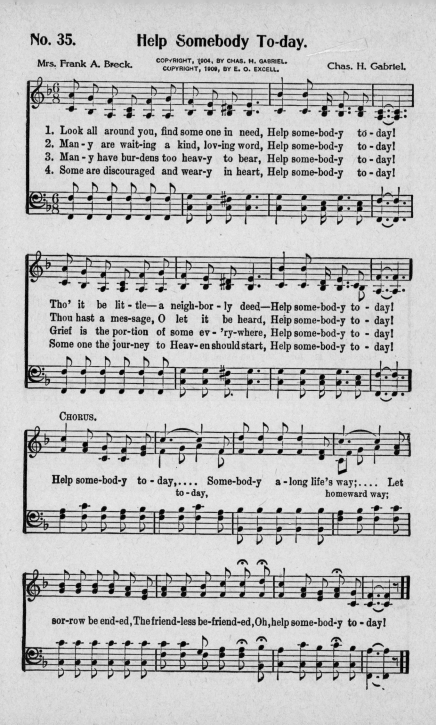

1. Look all around you, find some one in need, Help some-bod-y to - day!
2. Man - y are wait-ing a kind, lov-ing word, Help some-bod-y to - day!
3. Man - y have bur-dens too heav-y to bear, Help some-bod-y to - day!
4. Some are discouraged and wear-y in heart, Help some-bod-y to - day!

Tho' it be lit - tle—a neigh-bor - ly deed—Help some-bod-y to - day!
Thou hast a mes-sage, O let it be heard, Help some-bod-y to - day!
Grief is the por-tion of some ev - 'ry-where, Help some-bod-y to - day!
Some one the jour-ney to Heav-en should start, Help some-bod-y to - day!

CHORUS.

Help some-bod-y to - day,.... Some-bod-y a - long life's way;.... Let
to - day, homeward way;

sor-row be end-ed, The friend-less be-friend-ed, Oh, help some-bod-y to - day!

No. 36. What Wondrous Love.

COPYRIGHT, 1914, BY E. O. EXCELL.

John Newton.

E. O. Excell.

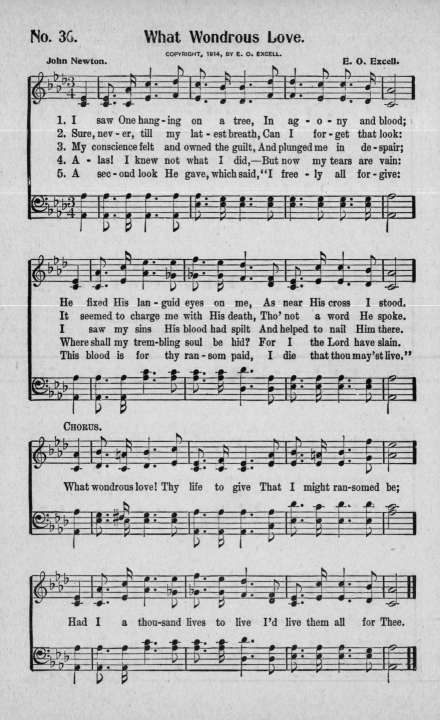

1. I saw One hang-ing on a tree, In ag-o-ny and blood;
2. Sure, nev-er, till my lat-est breath, Can I for-get that look:
3. My conscience felt and owned the guilt, And plunged me in de-spair;
4. A-las! I knew not what I did,—But now my tears are vain:
5. A sec-ond look He gave, which said, "I free-ly all for-give:

He fixed His lan-guid eyes on me, As near His cross I stood.
It seemed to charge me with His death, Tho' not a word He spoke.
I saw my sins His blood had spilt And helped to nail Him there.
Where shall my trem-bling soul be hid? For I the Lord have slain.
This blood is for thy ran-som paid, I die that thou may'st live."

CHORUS.

What wondrous love! Thy life to give That I might ran-somed be;

Had I a thou-sand lives to live I'd live them all for Thee.

No. 37. God Will Take Care of You.

Dedicated to my wife, Mrs. John A. Davis.

C. D. Martin.

COPYRIGHT, 1905, BY JOHN A. DAVIS.
USED BY PERMISSION.

W. S. Martin.

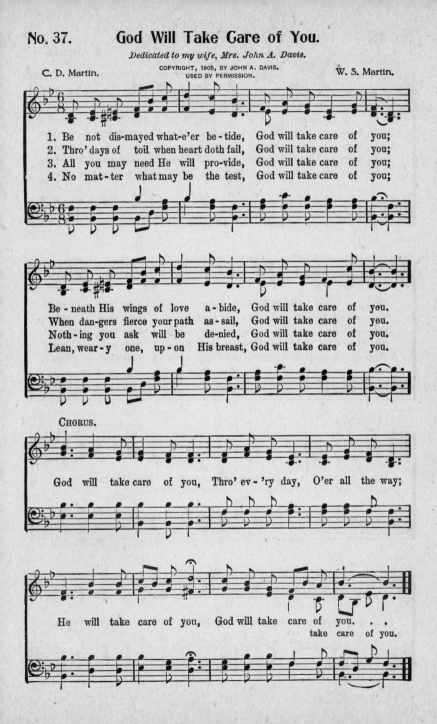

1. Be not dis-mayed what-e'er be-tide, God will take care of you;
2. Thro' days of toil when heart doth fail, God will take care of you;
3. All you may need He will pro-vide, God will take care of you;
4. No mat-ter what may be the test, God will take care of you;

Be - neath His wings of love a-bide, God will take care of you.
When dan-gers fierce your path as-sail, God will take care of you.
Noth-ing you ask will be de-nied, God will take care of you.
Lean, wear-y one, up-on His breast, God will take care of you.

CHORUS.

God will take care of you, Thro' ev-'ry day, O'er all the way;

He will take care of you, God will take care of you. . .
take care of you.

No. 38. Since I Have Been Redeemed.

E. O. E.

E. O. Excell.

1. I have a song I love to sing, Since I have been re-deemed,
2. I have a Christ that sat-is-fies, Since I have been re-deemed,
3. I have a Wit-ness bright and clear, Since I have been re-deemed,
4. I have a joy I can't ex-press, Since I have been re-deemed,
5. I have a home pre-pared for me, Since I have been re-deemed,

Of my Re-deem-er, Sav-ior, King, Since I have been re-deemed.
To do His will my high-est prize, Since I have been re-deemed.
Dis-pel-ling ev-'ry doubt and fear, Since I have been re-deemed.
All thro' His blood and right-eous-ness, Since I have been re-deemed.
Where I shall dwell e-ter-nal-ly, Since I have been re-deemed.

CHORUS.

Since I . . . . . have been redeemed, Since I have been redeemed,
Since I have been redeemed, Since I have been redeemed,

I will glo-ry in His name; I will glo-ry in my Sav-ior's name.

The Church in the Wildwood.

W. S. P.

NEW ARRANGEMENT OF WORDS AND MUSIC
COPYRIGHT, 1910, BY E. O. EXCELL.

Dr. William S. Pitts.

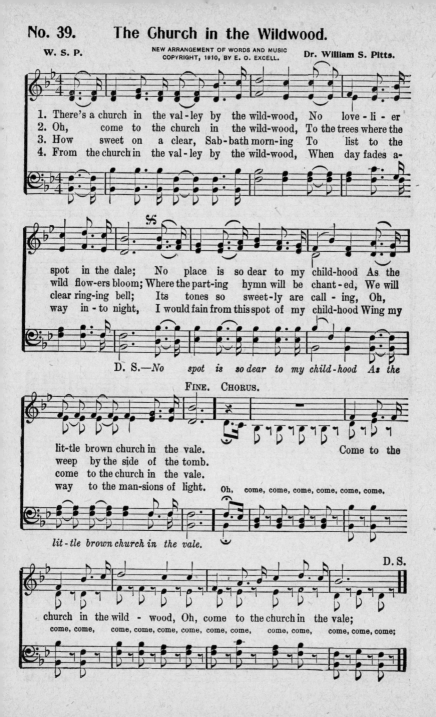

1. There's a church in the val-ley by the wild-wood, No love-li-er
2. Oh, come to the church in the wild-wood, To the trees where the
3. How sweet on a clear, Sab-bath morn-ing To list to the
4. From the church in the val-ley by the wild-wood, When day fades a-

spot in the dale; No place is so dear to my child-hood As the
wild flow-ers bloom; Where the part-ing hymn will be chant-ed, We will
clear ring-ing bell; Its tones so sweet-ly are call-ing, Oh,
way in-to night, I would fain from this spot of my child-hood Wing my

D. S.—*No spot is so dear to my child-hood As the*

FINE. CHORUS.

lit-tle brown church in the vale.
weep by the side of the tomb.
come to the church in the vale.
way to the man-sions of light.

Oh, come, come, come, come, come, come,

lit-tle brown church in the vale.

Come to the

D. S.

church in the wild-wood, Oh, come to the church in the vale;
come, come, come, come, come, come, come, come, come, come, come, come, come;

No. 40. Day is Dying in the West.

Mary Ann Lathbury.   William F. Sherwin.

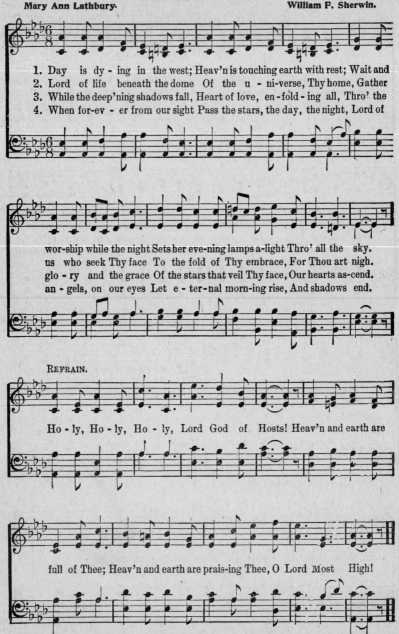

1. Day is dy - ing in the west; Heav'n is touching earth with rest; Wait and
2. Lord of life beneath the dome Of the u - ni-verse, Thy home, Gather
3. While the deep'ning shadows fall, Heart of love, en-fold-ing all, Thro' the
4. When for-ev - er from our sight Pass the stars, the day, the night, Lord of

wor-ship while the night Sets her eve-ning lamps a-light Thro' all the sky.
us who seek Thy face To the fold of Thy embrace, For Thou art nigh.
glo - ry and the grace Of the stars that veil Thy face, Our hearts as-cend.
an - gels, on our eyes Let e - ter-nal morn-ing rise, And shadows end.

REFRAIN.

Ho - ly, Ho - ly, Ho - ly, Lord God of Hosts! Heav'n and earth are

full of Thee; Heav'n and earth are prais-ing Thee, O Lord Most High!

No. 41. It Was His Love.

Rev. E. A. Hoffman.

Chas. H. Gabriel.

1. It was His love that reached my soul, It was His grace that made me whole,
2. It was His love, so boundless, free, That moved the Lord to par-don me
3. It was His love impelled my heart To turn from self and sin a part,
4. It was His great a-maz-ing love So well displayed from Heav'n a-bove,

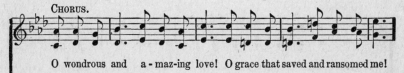

And now He keeps me day by day, And safe-ly leads me all the way.
And own me for His ransomed child, Redeemed, renewed and rec-on - ciled.
And find in Him the wondrous power A Christian life to live each hour.
That bro't to me such peace and rest, And made me so su-preme-ly blest.

CHORUS.

O wondrous and a - maz-ing love! O grace that saved and ransomed me!

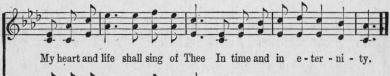

My heart and life shall sing of Thee In time and in e - ter - ni - ty.

No. 42.　Since I Found My Savior.

E. E. Hewitt.

Jno. R. Sweney.

1. Life wears a dif-f'rent face to me, Since I found my Sav-ior;
2. He sought me in His wondrous love, So I found my Sav-ior;
3. The pass-ing clouds may in-ter-vene, Since I found my Sav-ior,
4. A strong hand kind-ly holds my own, Since I found my Sav-ior;

Rich mer-cy at the cross I see, My dy-ing, liv-ing Sav-ior.
He brought sal-va-tion from a-bove, My dear, al-might-y Sav-ior.
But He is with me, tho' un-seen, My ev-er-pres-ent Sav-ior.
It leads me on-ward to the throne; O there I'll see my Sav-ior.

CHORUS.

Gold-en sun-beams 'round me play, Je-sus turns my night to day,

Heav-en seems not far a-way, Since I found my Sav-ior.

Tell It Wherever You Go.

Rev. Johnston Oatman, Jr.

Wm. Edie Marks.

1. If Christ the Re-deem-er has pardoned your sin, Tell it wher-ev-er you go;
2. If now you are happy with Christ as your Guide, Tell it wher-ev-er you go;
3. When troubles as-sail do you trust in Him still? Tell it wher-ev-er you go;
4. If you are an heir to a mansion on high, Tell it wher-ev-er you go;

If in-to your darkness His light has shown in, Tell it wher-ev-er you go.
If He is your Friend, and with Him you abide, Tell it wher-ev-er you go.
When sorrows o'erwhelm do you sink in His will? Tell it wher-ev-er you go.
Un - til you find rest in that home in the sky, Tell it wher-ev-er you go.

CHORUS.

Tell it,...... tell it,........ Tell it wher-ev - er you go; If
Tell it that others around you may know,

you would win oth-ers from sin and from woe, Tell it wher-ev-er you go!

No. 44. He is So Precious to Me.

C. H. G.

Chas. H. Gabriel.

1. So pre-cious is Je-sus, my Sav-ior, my King, His praise all the
2. He stood at my heart's door 'mid sunshine and rain, And pa-tient-ly
3. I stand on the moun-tain of bless-ing at last, No cloud in the
4. I praise Him be-cause He ap-point-ed a place Where, some day, thro'

day long with rapture I sing; To Him in my weakness for strength I can cling,
waited an entrance to gain; What shame that so long He en-treat-ed in vain,
heavens a shad-ow to cast; His smile is up-on me, the val-ley is past,
faith in His won-der-ful grace, I know I shall see Him—shall look on His face,

CHORUS. *Faster.*

For He is so precious to me.... For He is so precious to me,........
so pre-cious to me,

For He is so pre-cious to me;.......... 'Tis Heav-en be-low
so pre-cious to me;

rit. . . . .

My Re-deem-er to know, For He is so pre-cious to me.

Live in Sunshine.

Katharine A. Grimes.   Ira B. Wilson.

1. This world is not a place for gloom, While sunshine lights the morning sky,
2. This world is not a place for wrong While God's dear hand is o - ver all;
3. This world is not a place for tears While Je-sus comforts those who weep;
4. This world is not a place for sin, For shame, or sor-row, or de-spair,

While blossoms store their sweet perfume For ev-'ry one who passes by.
Go meet your sor - row with a song, And nothing e - vil shall be-fall.
Let hope and joy replace your fears—His watchful care your ways will keep.
While Je - sus' blood can make us clean, While He will all our burdens bear.

CHORUS.

Then let not grief your heart be - guile,..... Meet ev - 'ry trou - ble
be - guile,

with a smile;..... Are an - y sad,.......... go make them
a smile;   Are an - y sad,

glad,............. And live in sun - shine all the while.
go make them glad,

Jesus On the Cross.

Ina Duley Ogdon.

B. D. Ackley.

1. A vi - sion goes be - fore me, day by day, Je - sus, bless - ed
2. And when I see Him there in ag - o - ny, Je - sus, bless - ed
3. For me He came from glo - ry to the grave, Je - sus, bless - ed
4. Hence-forth that I my grat - i - tude may prove, Je - sus, bless - ed

Je - sus on the cross! It keeps me in the straight and nar - row way,
Je - sus on the cross! I mar - vel at His sac - ri - fice for me,
Je - sus on the cross! To save my soul His life for me He gave,
Je - sus on the cross! I con - se - crate to Him my heart of love,

REFRAIN.

Je - sus, bless-ed Je - sus on the cross! I see my lov-ing Sav-ior thro' my

tears; (thro' my tears;) His mem-o-ry I cher-ish all the years; (all the years;) My heart no

lon-ger fears, since His sac-ri-fice ap-pears, Je-sus, blessed Je-sus on the cross!

No. 47. Tell the Story.

Jennie Ree.

Ira B. Wilson.

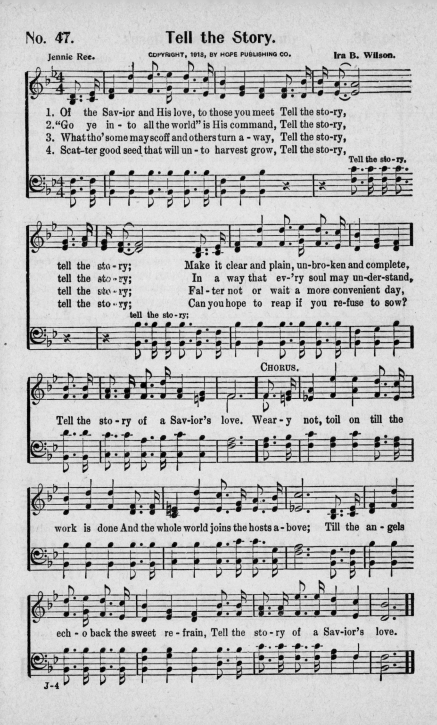

1. Of the Sav-ior and His love, to those you meet Tell the sto-ry,
2. "Go ye in-to all the world" is His command, Tell the sto-ry,
3. What tho' some may scoff and others turn a-way, Tell the sto-ry,
4. Scat-ter good seed that will un-to harvest grow, Tell the sto-ry,

Tell the sto-ry,

tell the sto-ry;   Make it clear and plain, un-bro-ken and complete,
tell the sto-ry;   In a way that ev-'ry soul may un-der-stand,
tell the sto-ry;   Fal-ter not or wait a more convenient day,
tell the sto-ry;   Can you hope to reap if you re-fuse to sow?

tell the sto-ry;

CHORUS.

Tell the sto-ry of a Sav-ior's love. Wear-y not, toil on till the
work is done And the whole world joins the hosts a-bove; Till the an-gels
ech-o back the sweet re-frain, Tell the sto-ry of a Sav-ior's love.

J-4

No. 48. Just the Love of Jesus.

James Rowe.

Wm. Edie Marks.

1. What is mak-ing life so sweet and bright to me? Just the love of Je - sus,
2. What af-fords me shel - ter when the tempest sweeps? Just the love of Je - sus,
3. What will help me tri-umph in this earth - ly strife? Just the love of Je - sus,
4. What will lead me safe a-cross the si - lent sea? Just the love of Je - sus,

just the love of Je-sus! What has made my soul so peaceful, pure, and free?
just the love of Je-sus! What, from day to day, my soul from e - vil keeps?
just the love of Je-sus! What is more to me than wealth, or fame, or life?
just the love of Je-sus! What will be my song thro' all e - ter - ni - ty?

CHORUS.

Just the love of Je - sus, my Sav - ior! Just the love of Je - sus,
O how sweet! Just the love of Je - sus makes my joy complete; What will guide my
soul to that safe re - treat? Just the love of Je - sus, my Sav - ior!

No. 49.   Because I Love Jesus.

James Rowe.

Chas. H. Gabriel.

1. My path may be lone-ly, and dark be the night, The clouds may be
2. Be-cause I love Je-sus, my Sav-ior and thine, There's peace in my
3. Tho' loved ones be ta-ken a-way from my side, Tho' rich-es and
4. Tho' all that is e-vil a-gainst me com-bine, Tho' Sa-tan a-

hid-ing the sun from my sight, Yet I have as-sur-ance that all will be right,
soul, there is comfort di-vine; 'Twill al-ways abide, for the promise is mine,
hon-or to me be de-nied, Yet if I but trust Him no ill can be-tide,
round me his snares should entwine, Yet if I am faith-ful a crown will be mine,

REFRAIN.

Be-cause...... I love Je-sus. Be-cause I love Je-sus,
Be-cause

Je-sus, Be-cause...... I love Je-sus; My soul is at
Be-cause

rest, and in Him I am blest, Be-cause...... I love Je-sus.
Be-cause

Growing Dearer Each Day.

C. H. G.

Chas. H. Gabriel.

1. How sweet is the love of my Savior! 'Tis bound-less and deep as the sea; And
2. I know He is ev-er be-side me! E-ter-ni-ty on-ly will prove The
3. Wher-ev-er He leads I will fol-low, Thro' sor-row, or shadow, or sun; And
4. Some day face to face I shall see Him, And oh, what a joy it will be To

best of it all, it is dai-ly Grow-ing sweet-er and sweeter to me.
height and the depth of His mercy, And the breadth of His in-fi-nite love.
tho' I be tried in the fur-nace, I can say, "Lord, Thy will be it done."
know that His love, now so precious, Will for-ev-er grow sweeter to me!

CHORUS.

Sweet-er and sweeter to me, ... Dear-er and
Sweet-er to me, grow-ing sweet-er to me. Dear-er each day,

dear-er each day; .... Oh, won-der-ful love of my
grow-ing dear-er each day; Oh, won-der-ful love, love of my

Sav-ior, Grow-ing dear-er each step of my way!
Sav-ior, Grow-ing dear-er and dear-er each step of my way!

No. 51. We Shall See the King Some Day.

L. E. J.

L. E. Jones.

1. Tho' the way we jour-ney may be oft-en drear, We shall see the
2. Aft-er pain and an-guish, aft-er toil and care, We shall see the
3. Aft-er foes are conquered, aft-er bal-tles won, We shall see the
4. There with all the loved ones who have gone be-fore, We shall see the

King some day; (some day;) On that bless-ed morning clouds will dis-ap-pear;
King some day; (some day;) Thro' the endless a-ges joy and blessing share,
King some day; (some day;) Aft-er strife is o-ver, aft-er set of sun,
King some day; (some day;) Sor-row past for-ev-er, on that peaceful shore,

Chorus.

We shall see the King some day. We shall see the King some day, (some day,)

We shall shout and sing some day; (some day;) Gathered 'round the throne,

When He shall call His own, We shall see the King some day.

No. 52. Land of the Unsetting Sun.

W. C. Martin.

Chas. H. Gabriel.

1. Some sweet day I shall en-ter a place, When the work of my life shall be
2. Yes,   the bur-dens of life can be borne, When I think of the prize to be
3. I   can peace-ful-ly welcome the night When the hours of my life shall be
4. O   what joy! mor-tal tongue cannot tell, With e-ter-ni-ty on-ly be-

done; . . A place that is filled with His mar-vel-ous grace, In the
won; . . Of the beau-ti-ful robe and the crown to be worn, In the
run; . . . It will bring me no grief, but su-per-nal de-light, In the
gun; . . One an-oth-er to meet, with the Sav-ior to dwell, In the

CHORUS.

land of the Un-set-ting Sun.   I shall dwell in the land of de-light . .
of de-light,

When my jour-ney on earth has been run; . . . In the land where there
jour - - ney   on earth has been run;

com-eth no sor-row, no night, In the land of the Un-set-ting Sun.

No. 53.   **The Hope Set Before You.**

Fanny J. Crosby.   COPYRIGHT, 1910, BY E. O. EXCELL.   E. O. Excell.
                        WORDS AND MUSIC.

1. Lay hold on the hope set before you, And let not a moment be lost,
2. Lay hold on the hope set before you, Of life that you now may receive,
3. Lay hold on the hope set before you, Of joy that no mortal can speak;
4. Lay hold on the hope set before you, A hope that is steadfast and sure;

The Sav-ior has purchased your ransom, But think what a price it hath cost!
If, glad-ly His mercy ac-cept-ing, You tru-ly repent and be-lieve.
It tell-eth of rest for the wear-y, Thro' Je-sus, the low-ly and meek.
O haste to the blessed Re-deem-er, The lov-ing, the perfect and pure.

CHORUS.

Lay hold...... on e-ter-nal sal-va-tion, Lay
Lay hold, lay hold............. on e-ter-nal sal-va-tion, Lay

hold.... on the gift of God's on-ly Son; Lay hold...... on His in-
hold, lay hold.......... on God's on-ly Son; Lay hold, lay hold..........

fi-nite mer-cy, Lay hold...... on the Might-y One!
on His mer-cy, Lay hold, lay hold on the Might-y One!

Nobody Told Me of Jesus.

Mrs. Frank A. Breck.

Chas. H. Gabriel.

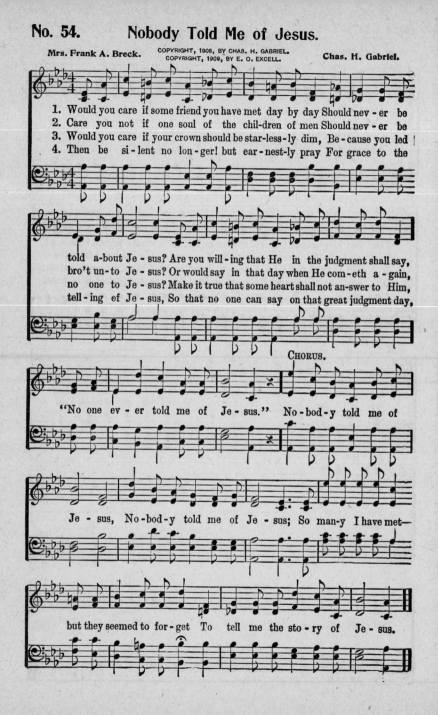

1. Would you care if some friend you have met day by day Should nev-er be
2. Care you not if one soul of the chil-dren of men Should nev-er be
3. Would you care if your crown should be star-less-ly dim, Be-cause you led
4. Then be si-lent no lon-ger! but ear-nest-ly pray For grace to the

told a-bout Je-sus? Are you will-ing that He in the judgment shall say,
bro't un-to Je-sus? Or would say in that day when He com-eth a-gain,
no one to Je-sus? Make it true that some heart shall not an-swer to Him,
tell-ing of Je-sus, So that no one can say on that great judgment day,

CHORUS.

"No one ev-er told me of Je-sus." No-bod-y told me of

Je-sus, No-bod-y told me of Je-sus; So man-y I have met—

but they seemed to for-get To tell me the sto-ry of Je-sus.

No. 55. Loyalty to Christ.

Dr. E. T. Cassel.

Flora H. Cassel.

1. From o - ver hill and plain There comes the signal strain, 'Tis loy-al-ty, loy-al-ty,
2. O hear, ye brave, the sound That moves the earth around, 'Tis loy-al-ty, loy-al-ty,
3. Come, join our loyal throng, We'll rout the gi-ant wrong, 'Tis loy-al-ty, loy-al-ty,
4. The strength of youth we lay At Je-sus' feet to-day, 'Tis loy-al-ty, loy-al-ty,

loy - al - ty to Christ; Its mu-sic rolls a - long, The hills take up the song,
loy - al - ty to Christ; A - rise to dare and do, Ring out the watch-word true,
loy - al - ty to Christ; Where Satan's banners float We'll send the bu - gle note,
loy - al - ty to Christ; His gos-pel we'll pro-claim Thro'-out the world's domain,

Chorus.

Of loy-al-ty, loy-al-ty, Yes, loy - al-ty to Christ; "On to vic-to-ry! On to

vic-to-ry!" Cries our great Commander; "On!". . . . We'll move at His command,
great Commander; "On!"

We'll soon pos-sess the land, Thro' loy-al-ty, loy-al-ty, Yes, loy-al-ty to Christ.

No. 56. God is Calling Yet.

Gerhard Tersteegen.   E. O. Excell.

1. God call-ing yet! shall I not hear? Earth's pleasures shall I still hold dear?
2. God call-ing yet! shall I not rise? Can I His lov-ing voice de-spise,
3. God call-ing yet! and shall He knock, And I my heart the clo-ser lock?
4. God call-ing yet! I can-not stay, My heart I yield with-out de-lay;

Shall life's swift pass-ing years all fly, And still my soul in slum-ber lie?
And base-ly His kind care re-pay? He calls me still; can I de-lay?
He still is wait-ing to re-ceive, And shall I dare His Spir-it grieve?
Vain world, farewell, from thee I part; The voice of God has reached my heart.

CHORUS.

Call - - ing, oh, hear Him call - - ing, oh, hear Him, God is
God is call-ing yet,   God is call-ing yet,

rit.   *a tempo.*

call - ing yet, oh, hear Him call-ing, call-ing; Call - - ing, oh, hear Him,
God is call-ing yet,

rit.

call - - ing, oh, hear Him, God is call-ing yet, oh, hear Him calling yet.
God is call-ing yet,

No. 57. Someone is Looking to You.

W. M. Lighthall.

Chas. H. Gabriel.

1. Let your light shine where-so-e'er you go, Some-one is look-ing to you! Bright-er each day let it gleam and glow, Some-one is look-ing to you!
2. Some-one is grop-ing his way to God, Some-one is look-ing to you! Fol-low-ing on where your feet have trod, Some-one is look-ing to you!
3. Some-one your coun-sel will sure-ly take, Some-one is look-ing to you! And by your life his de-ci-sion make, Some-one is look-ing to you!
4. Some-one has al-most ac-cept-ed Him, Some-one is look-ing to you! And may be lost if your light grows dim, Some-one is look-ing to you!

CHORUS.

Look-ing to you, yes, look-ing to you! Let your light shine the dark-ness through; O be faith-ful, be loy-al, and true, For some-one is look-ing to you!

No. 58. Alone With God.

G. H. C.   George H. Carr.

1. I love to be a-lone with God, And to lis-ten to His lov-ing voice;
2. I tell Him of my doubts and fears, And He stills the tempest in my breast,
3. I tell Him of my weak-ness-es, Of my sins, my hopes, my fond de-sires;
4. Then let me nev-er seek to know Sweeter friendship than with Him I find,

As He bids my ev'-ry care depart, How His presence makes my heart rejoice!
Bids the raging storms of passion cease, Calms my anxious tho't with quiet rest.
And He cheers my heart to onward press To gain the goal my soul as-pires.
As I choose the qui-et hours with Him, Leav-ing all the bus-y world be-hind.

CHORUS.

A-lone with God, No oth-er friend so dear, A-lone with
A-lone with God,   A-

God, What joy when He is near! My heart with rap-ture thrills,
lone with God,

My cup of bless-ing fills, When all a-lone with God.
When all a-lone with God.

No. 59. Let Jesus Come Into Your Heart.

COPYRIGHT, 1898, BY H. L. GILMOUR.
USED BY PERMISSION.

C. H. M. Mrs. C. H. Morris.

1. If you are tired of the load of your sin, Let Je-sus come in-to your heart; If you de-sire a new life to be-gin,
2. If 'tis for pu-ri-ty now that you sigh, Let Je-sus come in-to your heart; Fountains for cleansing are flow-ing near by,
3. If there's a tem-pest your voice can-not still, Let Je-sus come in-to your heart; If there's a void this world nev-er can fill,
4. If you would join the glad songs of the blest, Let Je-sus come in-to your heart; If you would en-ter the mansions of rest,

Let Je-sus come in-to your heart.

CHORUS.

Just now, your doubtings give o'er; Just now, re-ject Him no more; Just now, throw o-pen the door; Let Je-sus come in-to your heart.

All for Jesus.

Rev. J. B. Atchinson.

E. O. Excell.

1. All, yes, all I give to Je-sus, It belongs to Him;
2. All, yes, all I give to Je-sus, It belongs to Him;
3. All, yes, all I give to Je-sus, It belongs to Him;
4. All, yes, all I give to Je-sus, It belongs to Him;

All my heart I give to Je-sus, It be-longs to Him;
All my voice I give to Je-sus, It be-longs to Him;
All my love I give to Je-sus, It be-longs to Him;
All my life I give to Je-sus, It be-longs to Him;

Ev - er-more to be His dwell-ing, Ev - er-more His prais - es swell-ing,
Plead-ing for the young and hoar - y, Tell - ing of His pow'r and glo - ry,
Lov - ing Him for love un - ceas-ing, For His mer - cy e'er in-creas-ing,
Hour by hour I'll live for Je - sus, Day by day I'll work for Je - sus,

Ev - er-more His good - ness tell - ing,—It be-longs to Him.
Sing - ing o'er and o'er the sto - ry,—It be-longs to Him.
For His watch-care nev - er ceas-ing,—It be-longs to Him.
Ev - er-more I'll hon - or Je - sus,—It be-longs to Him.

We've a Story to Tell.

Colin Sterne.

H. E. Nichol.

Voices in Unison.

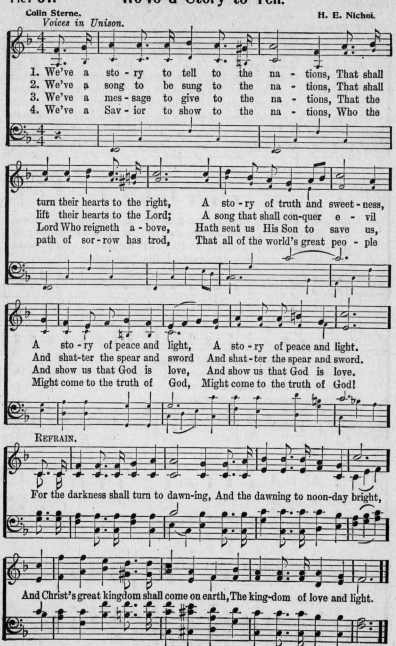

1. We've a sto-ry to tell to the na - tions, That shall
2. We've a song to be sung to the na - tions, That shall
3. We've a mes-sage to give to the na - tions, That the
4. We've a Sav-ior to show to the na - tions, Who the

turn their hearts to the right,   A sto-ry of truth and sweet-ness,
lift their hearts to the Lord;   A song that shall con-quer e - vil
Lord Who reigneth a - bove,   Hath sent us His Son to save us,
path of sor-row has trod,   That all of the world's great peo - ple

A sto-ry of peace and light,   A sto-ry of peace and light.
And shat-ter the spear and sword   And shat-ter the spear and sword.
And show us that God is love,   And show us that God is love.
Might come to the truth of God,   Might come to the truth of God!

REFRAIN.

For the darkness shall turn to dawn-ing, And the dawning to noon-day bright,

And Christ's great kingdom shall come on earth, The king-dom of love and light.

Stepping in the Light.

L. H. Edmunds.

Wm. J. Kirkpatrick.

1. Try - ing to walk in the steps of the Sav-ior, Try - ing to fol - low our
2. Press-ing more closely to Him who is lead - ing, When we are tempted to
3. Walk-ing in foot-steps of gen - tle forbearance, Foot-steps of faith-ful-ness,
4. Try - ing to walk in the steps of the Sav-ior, Up-ward, still up-ward we'll

Sav - ior and King; Shap-ing our lives by His bless - ed ex - am-ple,
turn from the way; Trust-ing the arm that is strong to de-fend us,
mer - cy, and love, Look-ing to Him for the grace free - ly promised,
fol - low our Guide, When we shall see Him, "the King in His beau-ty,"

CHORUS.

Hap-py, how happy, the songs that we bring.
Hap-py, how happy, our praises each day.   How beau-ti-ful to walk in the
Hap-py, how happy, our jour-ney a-bove.
Hap-py, how happy, our place at His side.

steps of the Sav - ior, Stepping in the light, Stepping in the light; How

beau-ti-ful to walk in the steps of the Sav-ior, Led in paths of light.

No. 63. Rescue the Perishing.

Fanny J. Crosby.

William H. Doane.

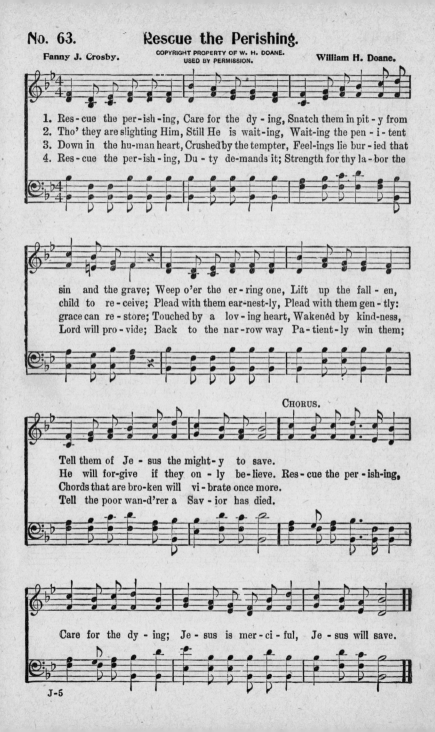

1. Res - cue the per - ish - ing, Care for the dy - ing, Snatch them in pit - y from
2. Tho' they are slighting Him, Still He is wait - ing, Wait - ing the pen - i - tent
3. Down in the hu - man heart, Crushed by the tempter, Feel - ings lie bur - ied that
4. Res - cue the per - ish - ing, Du - ty de - mands it; Strength for thy la - bor the

sin and the grave; Weep o'er the er - ring one, Lift up the fall - en,
child to re - ceive; Plead with them ear - nest - ly, Plead with them gen - tly:
grace can re - store; Touched by a lov - ing heart, Wakenèd by kind - ness,
Lord will pro - vide; Back to the nar - row way Pa - tient - ly win them;

CHORUS.

Tell them of Je - sus the might - y to save.
He will for - give if they on - ly be - lieve. Res - cue the per - ish - ing,
Chords that are bro - ken will vi - brate once more.
Tell the poor wan - d'rer a Sav - ior has died.

Care for the dy - ing; Je - sus is mer - ci - ful, Je - sus will save.

J-5

No. 64.   Servant of God. Awake.

Charlotte G. Homer.

Chas. H. Gabriel.

1. Serv - ant of God, a - wake un - to thy du - ty; Why will ye
2. Wide are the plains that glimm'ring lie be - fore thee Ripe un - to
3. Up! in the name of Him who died to save you; Seek for the
4. "He that en - dur - eth," is the word re - cord - ed, Shall joy and

doubt, why fal - ter, why de - lay?   Look on the fields that wave in
har - vest; thrust the sick - le in!   High in the heav'ns the sun is
er - ring as He sought for you!   Al - ways re - mem - ber what in
ev - er - last - ing life ob - tain;   To him a crown at last shall

gold - en beau - ty, While thou art dream - ing pre - cious hours a - way.
burn - ing o'er thee,—Still thou art i - dle! Now the work be - gin.
love He gave you, And be a serv - ant, loy - al, brave, and true.
be a - ward - ed, Thro' Christ the Lord, who was for sin - ners slain.

CHORUS.

Serv - ant of God, a - rouse ye, a - wake! Je - sus is call - ing! Go,

la - bor for His sake! Je - sus is call - ing! Go, la - bor for His sake!

No. 65. A Little Bit of Love.

To my Friend, Marion Lawrance.

E. O. E.   E. O. Excell.

1. Do you know the world is dy-ing For a lit-tle bit of love? Ev-'ry-
2. From the poor of ev-'ry cit-y, For a lit-tle bit of love, Hands are
3. Down be-fore their i-dols fall-ing, For a lit-tle bit of love, Man-y
4. While the souls of men are dy-ing For a lit-tle bit of love, While the

where we hear the sigh-ing For a lit-tle bit of love; For the love that rights a
reach-ing out in pit-y For a lit-tle bit of love; Some have burdens hard to
souls in vain are call-ing For a lit-tle bit of love; If they die in sin and
chil-dren, too, are cry-ing For a lit-tle bit of love, Stand no lon-ger i-dly

wrong, Fills the heart with hope and song; They have waited, oh, so long, For a
bear, Some have sorrows we should share; Shall they falter and de-spair For a
shame, Some one sure-ly is to blame For not go-ing in His name, With a
by, You can help them if you try; Go, then, saying, "Here am I," With a

FINE.   REFRAIN.   *D. S. each verse.*

lit-tle bit of love. For a lit-tle bit of love, For a lit-tle bit of love.
lit-tle bit of love? For a lit-tle bit of love, For a lit-tle bit of love.
lit-tle bit of love. With a lit-tle bit of love, With a lit-tle bit of love.
lit-tle bit of love. With a lit-tle bit of love, With a lit-tle bit of love.

O Gift Divine.

Geo. O. Webster, alt. COPYRIGHT, 1913, BY HOPE PUBLISHING CO. Ira B. Wilson.

1. O gift di-vine, God's boundless love re-veal-ing To ev-'ry wand'ring
2. O wondrous love, proclaimed in song and sto-ry, So full, so free to
3. My theme in life shall be my Savior's prais-es; I'll tell His love and

soul by sin op-pressed; O heart of mine, o'er ev'ry chord comes stealing
all the sons of men! From Heav'n above, from throne of brightest glo-ry,
nev-er-end-ing peace; My hap-py heart un-ceas-ing-ly up-rais-es

CHORUS.

The joy I felt when first I found that rest.   O heart of mine,......
I hear it ring with-in my soul a-gain.
A song of joy that never-more shall cease.   O heart of mine,

this gift di-vine........   Is pledge of love un-told;.......Break forth in
        this gift di-vine,   the pledge of love un-told;

song........ and speed a-long......,   The sto-ry sweet and old.
Break forth in song   and speed along

No. 67. Somewhere.

James Rowe.   B. D. Ackley.

1. Some-where, be-yond the hills of life, And all the bounds of sin and strife; Where gates are pearl and streets are gold, My Sav-ior I shall then be-hold.

2. Some-where, the an-gels sing His praise, And throngs their glad ho-san-nas raise; The hands once nailed to Cal-v'ry's tree Will be out-stretched to welcome me.

3. Some-where, my life so sweet and fair, His glo-ry I shall al-ways share; And there with Him and all the blest, For-ev-er-more my soul shall rest.

sin and strife;

CHORUS.

Some-where, I know that I shall see,— Je-sus,— who gave His life for me; Some-where, when He will call me, I will go To Him, be-cause He loves me so.

No. 68. Drive It Away With a Song.

E. E. Hewitt.

B. D. Ackley.

1. What tho' a cloud should sweep o-ver your sky, Veil-ing the sun-beams that
2. Has some resentment wrought strife and ill-will? Love and for-give-ness work
3. Sing of the bless-ings, so man-y and sweet, Like heav'nly blos-soms that

spark-le on high?— Fear not, the shad-ow will pass by and by;
mir-a-cles still; Let no wrong-feel-ing your cup of life fill,
smile 'round your feet; And if some grievance per-chance you may meet,

CHORUS.

Drive it a-way with a song........ Drive it a-way,
a song.

drive it a-way, Love will the ech-oes pro-long; Sing on with

glad-ness, ban-ish your sad-ness, Drive it a-way with a song.

No. 69. In His Keeping.

Mrs C H M.

Mrs. C. H. Morris

1. When the ear - ly morning breaking, Slumber from my eye-lids shak-ing, Comes the
2. Some-times dark clouds hang o'er me, Not one step I see be - fore me, Still, my
3. Gen - tle e - ven-tide is near-ing, Light from Heaven dis-ap-pear-ing, Still the

bless-ed tho't with wak-ing, I am in His keep-ing. Day ad-vanc-es, la-bor
Sav - ior, I a - dore Thee, I am in His keep-ing. I can trust His hand to
bless-ed tho't so cheer - ing, I am in His keeping. Now night's curtains gather

bring-ing, Care, her mantle 'round me flinging, Yet midst all my soul keeps singing,
guide me, 'Neath His wings He'll safely hide me, And no harm can e'er be-tide me,
'round me, Yet its dan-gers have not found me, For His angel guards surround me,

CHORUS.

I am in His care. I am in my Fa-ther's keep-ing, I am in His

rit.

ten - der care; Wheth-er wak-ing, wheth-er sleep-ing, I am in His care.

No. 70. Christ Shall Be King.

W. C. Poole.

COPYRIGHT, 1913, BY CHAS. H. GABRIEL.
E. O. EXCELL, OWNER.

Chas. H. Gabriel.

1. Christ shall be King of the whole wide world, He shall be King, let prais-es ring!
2. Christ shall be King o - ver land and sea, He shall be King, let prais-es ring!
3. Christ shall be King in my heart to - day, He shall be King, let prais-es ring!

Un-der His banner of love unfurled, There shall be gathered the whole wide world.
He who redeemed us and made us free, King of the world shall for-ev - er be,
O-ver each tho't and each purpose sway, All that I have shall be His al - way,

rit.

CHORUS.

And Christ shall be the King. O - ver all the world Christ shall be the King;
Yes, Christ shall be the King.
For Christ shall be the King. O - ver all the world Christ shall be the King;

O - ver all the world let His praises ring; Ev'ry land and nation Shall
O - ver all the world let His prais-es ring;

know His great sal-va-tion; Christ shall be the King, He shall be the King.

No. 71. The Way of the Cross Leads Home.

Jessie Brown Pounds.

Chas. H. Gabriel.

1. I must needs go home by the way of the cross, There's no oth-er
2. I must needs go on in the blood-sprinkled way, The path that the
3. Then I bid fare-well to the way of the world, To walk in it

way but this; I shall ne'er get sight of the Gates of Light,
Sav-ior trod, If I ev-er climb to the heights sub-lime,
nev-er more; For my Lord says "Come," and I seek my home,

CHORUS.

If the way of the cross I miss.
Where the soul is at home with God. The way of the cross leads
Where He waits at the o-pen door.

home, The way of the cross leads home; It is
leads home, leads home;

sweet to know, as I on-ward go, The way of the cross leads home.

No. 72. In the Cleft of the Rock.

Lizzie DeArmond.

J. S. Fearis.

1. High as the mountain tho' the bil-lows roll, In Je-sus' keep-ing
2. O soul, be faith-ful; to the end en-dure, Trust-ing His prom-is-
3. When thro' the Jor-dan I must take my way, His staff will com-fort

I will trust my soul; He can the rag-ing seas and wind con-trol,
es for-ev-er sure; Kept in the fort-ress of His love se-cure.
me and be my stay; O-ver the riv-er there is end-less day,

REFRAIN.

In the cleft of the Rock He will hide me. Hide . . . me, safe-ly

Hide me, safe-ly hide,

hide me, Hide . . . me, safe-ly hide me,

hide . . . . me, safe-ly hide, ... Hide . . . . me, safe-ly

hide me, safe-ly hide, Hide me, safe-ly hide, hide me in the Rock.

Hide . . . me from all dan-ger, In the Rock that was cleft for me.

Hide me from all dan-ger, from all dan-ger.

No. 73. O That Will Be Glory.

C. H. G. Chas. H. Gabriel.

1. When all my la-bors and tri-als are o'er, And I am safe on that
beau-ti-ful shore, Just to be near the dear Lord I a-dore,
Will thro' the a-ges be glo-ry for me.

2. When, by the gift of His in-fi-nite grace, I am ac-cord-ed in
Heav-en a place, Just to be there and to look on His face,
Will thro' the a-ges be glo-ry for me.

3. Friends will be there I have loved long a-go; Joy like a riv-er a-
round me will flow; Yet, just a smile from my Sav-ior, I know,
Will thro' the a-ges be glo-ry for me.

rit. CHORUS. _Faster._

O that will be glo-ry for me, Glo-ry for me, glo-ry for me;
O . . . . that will be glo-ry for me, Glo-ry for me, glo-ry for me; . . . .

When by His grace I shall look on His face, That will be glo-ry, be glo-ry for me.

No. 74. In His Sunlight.

James Rowe.

B. D. Ackley.

1. In the light and glo - ry of His life and sto - ry There is
2. O my bless - ed Sav - ior! He is mine for - ev - er, And will
3. Oh, the peace and pleas-ure, oh, the price-less treas-ure Of the

ev - 'ry-thing that I can need; That is why I'm cling-ing and His
be my near - est, dear - est Friend; That is why I love Him, hav-ing
love of Him who died for me! Thro' that day e - ter - nal, in the

CHORUS.

prais - es sing-ing, As the lost to Him I lead.
naught above Him, And shall trust Him to the end. In His sunlight, His precious
world su - per-nal, Love Di-vine my song shall be.

sun-light, I am al - ways hap - py, yes, in - deed! In His sun-light,

His pre-cious sun - light, There is ev - 'ry-thing I need.

No. 75. The King's Business.

COPYRIGHT, 1902, BY E. O. EXCELL.
WORDS AND MUSIC.

Dr. E. T. Cassel.   Flora H. Cassel.

1. I am a stran-ger here, with-in a for-eign land; My home is
2. This is the King's command: that all men, ev - 'ry-where, Re-pent and
3. My home is bright-er far than Shar-on's ro - sy plain, E - ter - nal

far a-way, up-on a gold-en strand; Am - bas - sa - dor to be
turn a-way from sin's se - duc-tive snare; That all who will o-bey,
life and joy thro'-out its vast do-main; My Sov'reign bids me tell

of realms be-yond the sea, I'm here on business for my King.
with Him shall reign for aye, And that's my business for my King.
how mor-tals there may dwell, And that's my business for my King.

CHORUS.

This is the mes-sage that I bring, A message angels fain would sing; "Oh, be ye

reconciled," Thus saith my Lord and King, "Oh, be ye rec-on-ciled to God."

No. 76. Faith Will Bring the Blessing.

James Rowe.   B. D. Ackley.

1. If you need up-lift-ing, if you need a song, Strength to help your soul to
2. In some hour un-guard-ed, if the foe as-sail, Tho' you feel your weakness,
3. On the Lord de-pend-ing, sing a-long the way, Naught can ev-er harm you

tri-umph o-ver wrong, Put your faith in Je-sus, He is true and strong;
let not cour-age fail; Trust in Je-sus on-ly and you shall pre-vail;
if He is your stay; Lean up-on His promise till the bet-ter day;

CHORUS.

Faith will bring the blessing ev-'ry time . . Faith will bring the blessing
yes, ev'ry time.

ev'ry time, Tho' your faith be simple or sublime; For the Savior knows the heart.

Ev-'ry need He will impart; Faith will bring the blessing ev'ry time. . .
ev'ry time.

He is Able to Deliver Thee.

W. A. O.

W. A. Ogden.

1. 'T is the grand-est theme thro' the a - ges rung; 'T is the grand-est theme for a mor-tal tongue; 'T is the grandest theme that the world e'er sung,

2. 'T is the grand-est theme in the earth or main; 'T is the grand-est theme for a mor-tal strain; 'T is the grandest theme, tell the world a - gain,

3. 'T is the grand-est theme, let the ti - dings roll To the guilt - y heart, to the sin - ful soul; Look to God in faith, He will make thee whole,

CHORUS.

"Our God is a - ble to de-liv-er thee." He is a - - - ble to de-liv - er thee, He is a - - ble to de - liv - er thee; Tho' by sin op-prest, Go to Him for rest, "Our God is a - ble to de - liv - er thee."

a - ble, He is a - ble, He is a - ble

No. 78.   'Tis Sweet to Know.

W. L. T.

Will L. Thompson.

1. 'Tis sweet to know that Je-sus loves me, O how sweet! To know that I may
2. 'Tis sweet to know Him when life's sorrows Must be borne; To hear His cheering
3. 'Tis sweet to hear His in - vi - ta-tion,"Come to Me,""Come, all ye wear-y,

rest my bur-dens at His feet. O - ver us He's kind-ly watching,
words of com-fort when we mourn: Precious tho't that He is with us,
la - den ones, there's rest for thee." Je - sus' love is all-per-vad-ing,

Call - ing tow'rd the sky; O that all might heed His call and to Him fly.
At the o-pen grave, Al-ways read-y, ev - er will-ing us to save.
Thro'-out earth and sky; Hap - py they who know this love from God on high.

CHORUS.

This love   is mine,   I hear the Sav - ior call - ing;

This love   is mine

He of - fers you this bless - ing too, 'Tis free   to   all.

No. 79. The Home of Endless Years.

John R. Clements.

John R. Sweney.

1. Tho' bur-dens heav-y we here must bear, And the eyes are made
2. With toil-some ef-fort in faith we sow, Tho' no har-vest our
3. We'll la-bor with a smile and a song, And we'll give to the

dim with tears, There'll be naught of sor-row "o-ver there" In the
vi-sion cheers; We will not lose heart, 'twill all be plain, In the
winds our fears, For the day of tri-als can't be long, Soon the

CHORUS.

"home of the end-less years." In the bet-ter land, In that sun-ny land,

In that E-den land, safe by and by; In that bet-ter land,

In that sun-ny land, In that E-den land, safe by and by.

J-6

No. 80. Working, Watching, Praying.

Mrs. Frank A. Breck.

Powell G. Fithian.

1. Go forth! Go forth for Je-sus now, Be work-ing! Be watch-ing! The
2. Go forth! Go forth to all the world, O stay not! De-lay not! But
3. Go forth! Let heart and hand be strong! Be work-ing! Be watch-ing! O

Go forth!   Go forth!

Lord Him-self will teach you how To watch and pray. 'Tis not for thee thy
let love's ban-ner be unfurled, And grace be told. O let re-deem-ing
stay the mighty pow'r of wrong Wher-e'er ye may. Equipped with love and

field to choose; No work He gives must thou re-fuse; Be work-ing! Be watch-ing!
love be sung, A song of joy on ev-'ry tongue; Be work-ing! Be watch-ing!
strength divine, The vic-to-ry is sure-ly thine; Be work-ing! Be watch-ing!

CHORUS.

Be pray - ing! Go forth to work, to watch and pray! 'Tis Je-sus who calls thee;

Go forth!   Go forth!

The har-vest waits for thee to-day, Go bring some sheaves for God.

No. 81. Will There Be Any Stars?

E. E. Hewitt.   Jno. R. Sweney.

1. I am think-ing to-day of that beau-ti-ful land I shall reach when the
2. In the strength of the Lord let me la - bor and pray, Let me watch as a
3. Oh, what joy it will be when His face I be-hold, Liv-ing gems at His

sun go-eth down; When thro' won-der-ful grace by my Sav-ior I stand,
win-ner of souls; That bright stars may be mine in the glo-ri-ous day,
feet to lay down; It would sweet-en my bliss in the cit-y of gold,

CHORUS.

Will there be an - y stars in my crown?
When His praise like the sea-bil-low rolls. Will there be an-y stars, an-y
Should there be an - y stars in my crown.

stars in my crown When at evening the sun go-eth down? ... When I
go - eth down?

wake with the blest In the mansions of rest, Will there be any stars in my crown?
an - y stars in my crown?

No. 82.   Satisfied.

A. H. Ackley.

B. D. Ackley.

1. When I have fin-ished my pil-grim-age here, When shall have vanished temp-
2. When I am troub-led by grief and de-spair, Grace nev-er-fail-ing a-
3. When I have trav-eled the way with my Lord, Count-ing the mile-posts by

ta - tion and fear, As in the arms of His love I a - bide,
waits me up there; Will-ing to trust Him what-ev - er be - tide,
faith in His word, Liv-ing and dy - ing with Him at my side,

CHORUS.

I shall be sat - is - fied. I............. shall be sat - is -
I shall be sat - is - fied, I shall be

fied, I............. shall be sat - is - fied;
sat - is - fied, I shall be sat - is - fied, I shall be sat - is - fied;

rit.

Shel-tered a-bove by His in - fi - nite love, I shall be sat - is - fied.

No. 83. Nothing Satisfies but Jesus.

C. H. M.

Mrs. C. H. Morris.

1. Noth-ing sat-is-fies but Je-sus, Bread of life to mor-tals giv'n;
2. Since I heard the voice of Je-sus, Since mine eyes be-held the King,
3. With His joy my heart is thrill-ing, All my hope in Him I see;

May His pres-ence now re-fresh us Like the morn-ing dew from heav'n!
All my love, my heart's af-fec-tion, All I have, to Him I bring.
Doubt, and gloom, and fear dis-pel-ling, Christ is All in all to me.

CHORUS.

Give me Je-sus, give me Je-sus, Take the world, but give me Je-sus,
Give me Je-sus, give me Je-sus,

To sat-is-fy with ev-'ry bless-ing, His love and peace my soul pos-sess-ing;

To all be-side, my heart re-plies: There's naught but Je-sus sat-is-fies!

No. 84. In the Shadow of His Wings.

Rev. J. B. Atchinson. COPYRIGHT, 1910, BY E. O. EXCELL RENEWAL. E. O. Excell.

1. In the shad-ow of His wings There is rest, sweet rest; There is
2. In the shad-ow of His wings There is peace, sweet peace, Peace that
3. In the shad-ow of His wings There is joy, glad joy; There is

rest from care and la-bor, There is rest for friend and neighbor; In the
pass-eth un-der-stand-ing, Peace, sweet peace that knows no ending; In the
joy to tell the sto-ry, Joy ex-ceed-ing, full of glo-ry; In the

shad-ow of His wings There is rest, sweet rest, In the shadow of His wings
shad-ow of His wings There is peace, sweet peace, In the shadow of His wings
shad-ow of His wings There is joy, glad joy, In the shadow of His wings

CHORUS.

There is rest(sweet rest). There is rest, There is peace, There is
There is peace(sweet peace).
There is joy (glad joy). sweet rest. sweet peace.

joy, In the shad-ow of His wings; shad-ow of His wings.
glad joy.

"At Calvary."

Mrs. C. H. M.

Mrs. C. H. Morris.

1. By sin's con-dem-na-tion my heart was op-pressed, No peace could I
2. I plunged in the foun-tain, the rem-e-dy sure For sin and un-
3. Oh, won-der-ful cross with its arms stretching wide For you and for

find, and no com-fort, no rest, Till Je-sus' voice whis-pered so
clean-ness,—the un-fail-ing cure: My bur-den fell off,—and to
me, and the whole world be-side: No one is ex-clud-ed, and

sweet-ly to me, "Come lay down your bur-den at Cal-va-ry."
day I can see There's per-fect sal-va-tion at Cal-va-ry.
mer-cy is free For ev-'ry lost sin-ner at Cal-va-ry.

CHORUS.   cres.

At Cal-va-ry, at Cal-va-ry, My burdens fell off and from sin I was free; To

Je-sus for-ev-er the glo-ry shall be; I lost all my bur-dens at Cal-va-ry.

No. 86.   Keep the Heart Singing.

C. H. G.   Chas. H. Gabriel.

1. We may light-en toil and care, Or a heav-y bur-den share, With a
2. If His love is in the soul, And we yield to His con-trol, Sweetest
3. How a word of love will cheer, Kin-dle hope, and ban-ish fear, Soothe a

word, a kind-ly deed, or sun-ny smile; We may gir-dle day and night
mu-sic will the lone-ly hours be-guile; We may drive the clouds a-way,
pain, or take a-way the sting of guile; Oh, how much we all may do,

With a ha-lo of de-light, If we keep the heart singing all the while.
Cheer and bless the darkest day, If we keep the heart singing all the while.
In the world we trav-el thro', If we keep the heart singing all the while

Chorus.

Keep the heart singing all the while;....... Make the world brighter with a
sing-ing,   singing all the while;   bright-er,

smile;........ Keep the song ringing! lone-ly hours we may be-guile.
bright-er with a smile;

Scatter Sunshine.

Lanta Wilson Smith.

E. O. Excell.

1. In a world where sor-row Ev - er will be known, Where are found the
2. Slightest ac - tions oft - en Meet the sor - est needs, For the world wants
3. When the days are gloom-y Sing some hap-py song; Meet the world's re-

need - y And the sad and lone, How much joy and com - fort
dai - ly Lit - tle kind - ly deeds; Oh, what care and sor - row
pin - ing With a cour - age strong; Go with faith un - daunt - ed

You can all be - stow, If you scat-ter sun-shine Ev-'ry-where you go.
You may help re - move, With your songs and courage, Sym-pa-thy and love.
Thro' the ills of life; Scat-ter smiles and sunshine O'er its toil and strife.

CHORUS.

Scat - - ter sun-shine all a - long your way,..... Cheer and bless and
Scat-ter the smiles and sun-shine all a - long, o - ver the way,

1. bright - en Ev - 'ry pass-ing day;.....
   pass-ing day;
2. Ev - 'ry pass-ing day.

No. 88. I Will Not Forget Thee.

C. H. G.

Chas. H. Gabriel.

1. Sweet is the promise—"I will not forget thee," Nothing can mo-lest or turn my soul a-way; E'en tho' the night be dark with-in the val-ley, Just be-yond is shining one e-ter-nal day.

2. Trust-ing the promise—"I will not forget thee," Onward will I go with songs of joy and love; Tho' earth de-spise me, tho' my friends forsake me, I shall be remembered in my home above.

3. When at the gold-en por-tals I am standing, All my trib-u-la-tions all my sorrows past, How sweet to hear the bless-ed proc-la-ma-tion, "Enter, faithful servant, welcome home at last!"

CHORUS.

I . . . . . . will not forget thee or leave thee; In my hands I'll hold thee, in my arms I'll fold thee; I . . . . will not for-get thee or leave thee; I am thy Re-deem-er, I will care for thee.

I will not forget thee, I will nev-er leave thee; I will not for-get thee, for-get thee;

No. 89. Thy Kingdom Come.

Rev. C. McKibbin.

Chas. H. Gabriel.

1. Thy kingdom come! and shall not each one sing it, On land and sea, where'er His
2. Thy kingdom come! O haste to tell the message, The world is dy-ing for the
3. Thy kingdom come! He waits to bless the nations,'Tis ours to bring them quickly

ban-ner goes? Thy kingdom come! shall we not strive to bring it, The grace that
word of God; Send out the light, that Christ may see the fruitage, The world re-
to His feet; Make this the time to tram-ple sin's foundations, And lead the

saves the world from hu-man woes?
deemed that His own feet have trod. Thy kingdom come! the glo-rious tri-umph
er - ring to the mer-cy-seat.

CHORUS.

has-ten, When peoples all shall crown Him King of kings; . . . Saints shall re-
shall crown Him King of kings;

joice, and angels stop to lis-ten, While earth His ev-er-last-ing glo-ry sings.

No. 90. Where He Leads I'll Follow.

W. A. O. COPYRIGHT, 1885, BY W. A. OGDEN. W. A. Ogden.

1. Sweet are the prom-is-es, Kind is the word; Dear-er far than
2. Sweet is the ten-der love Je-sus hath shown, Sweet-er far than
3. List to His lov-ing words, "Come un-to me!" Wear-y, heav-y-

an-y mes-sage man ev-er heard; Pure was the mind of Christ,
an-y love that mor-tals have known; Kind to the err-ing one,
lad-en, there is sweet rest for thee; Trust in His prom-is-es,

Sin-less, I see; He the great ex-am-ple is, and pat-tern for me.
Faith-ful is He; He the great ex-am-ple is, and pat-tern for me.
Faith-ful and sure; Lean up-on the Sav-ior, and thy soul is se-cure.

CHORUS.

Where . . . . He leads I'll fol - - - low,
Where He leads I'll fol-low, Where He leads I'll fol-low,

Fol - - low all the way; Follow Jesus ev-'ry day.
Fol-low all the way, yes, fol-low all the way;

He Loves Everybody.

James Rowe.   B. D. Ackley.

1. In the hour of troub-le, it is sweet to have a friend, Some one who is
2. When the storm is sweeping, and the world seems most unjust, When some great mis-
3. When our souls are tempted, when we reach the sink-ing sand, And our hearts are

al-ways glad a help-ing hand to lend; One up-on whose faith-ful-ness we
for-tune comes and fail you think you must, There's a strong De-fend-er we may
long-ing for a kind, up-lift-ing hand, Look-ing for a Help-er who will

ev-er may de-pend; Such a friend is al-ways found in Je-sus.
safe-ly, sure-ly trust; Such a friend is al-ways found in Je-sus.
give us strength to stand; Such a friend is al-ways found in Je-sus.

CHORUS.

He loves ev-'ry-bod-y, He loves you; He loves ev-'ry-bod-y, you should too;

There will nev-er be a friend more true; He loves ev-'ry-bod-y, He loves you.

No. 92. The Wonderful Story.

C. H. G.

Chas. H. Gabriel.

1. O sweet is the sto-ry of Je-sus, The won-der-ful Sav-ior of men,
2. He came from the brightest of glo-ry; His blood as a ran-som He gave,
3. His mer-cy flows on like a riv-er; His love is unmeasured and free;

Who suf-fered and died for the sin-ner,—I'll tell it a-gain and a - gain!
To pur-chase e-ter-nal redemption; And, O He is mighty to save!
His grace is for-ev-er suf-fi-cient, It reach-es and pu-ri-fies me.

CHORUS.

O won - der-ful, wonderful sto - ry, The dear - est that
O won-der-ful sto - - ry, O won-der-ful sto - ry, The dear-est that ev - -

ev - er was told; . . I'll re-peat it in glo - ry, The wonderful
er, that ev - er was told; I'll re-peat it in glo - ry, The

sto - - ry, Where I . . shall His beau-ty be - hold. . .
won-der-ful sto - ry, Where I shall His beau - - ty, His beau-ty be - hold.

rit.

No. 93. His Love Is All I Need.

E. O. E.

E. O. Excell.

1. The love of Je-sus, who can tell, Tho' he may know it, oh, so well?
2. The love of Je-sus, oh, what bliss, To hear Him whis-per, I am His!
3. The love of Je-sus, oh, how sweet, To hide in such a safe re-treat!

The love that ev-'ry want sup-plies, The love that al-ways sat-is-fies;
Tho' I may fal-ter on the way, He will not let me go a-stray;
Tho' Sa-tan would my hopes de-stroy, My Savior's love is still my joy;

rit. CHORUS.

His love is all I need! So won-der-ful, His love to me!

More won-der-ful how could it be? My ev-'ry sin on Him was laid;

rit.

My ev-'ry debt by Him was paid; His love is all I need!

No. 94. Don't Forget to Pray.

Miriam E. Arnold.

Chas. H. Gabriel.

1. When the day is dark and lone - ly, Don't for - get to pray;
2. When the sun is bright - ly shin - ing, Don't for - get to pray;
3. O the bliss this won - drous friend-ship Will your soul af - ford,

Prayer will make your path - way bright - er, Drive the clouds a - way.
Let the Sav - ior share your glad - ness, On your pil - grim way;
Dwell - ing thus in close com - mun - ion With your lov - ing Lord;

For your lov - ing heav'n - ly Fa - ther Lis - tens when you call,
For He longs to walk be - side you, Your most trust - ed Friend,
Till in Heav'n you shall be - hold Him, See Him face to face,

FINE.

And in mer - cy He will an - swer, Trust Him for it all.
And a - bide thro' storm and sun-shine To your jour-ney's end.
And thro'-out e - ter - nal a - ges Praise Him for His grace.

D.S.—"In the se - cret of His pres - ence," Don't for - get to pray.

CHORUS.

D.S.

Tell Him all your sor - rows, He will turn your night to day,

No. 95. Saints in Glory.

COPYRIGHT, 1899, BY E. O. EXCELL.
WORDS AND MUSIC.

C. Bissett.

Chas. H. Gabriel.

1. Thy saints all stand in glo - ry Before Thy throne, O God, And sing un - to their
2. All clothed in robes of whiteness, They worship and a - dore, And fall be - fore their
3. Je - sus, my Lord and Sav - ior, Who bled and died for me, Who bore my sins and

Sav - ior, Who bo't them with His blood; And there in Heaven's glo - ry, From
Sav - ior, And praise Him ev - er - more; There, lifting up their voi - ces, With
sor - rows On the ac - curs - ed tree; I, too, shall stand in glo - ry, And

sin and sor-row free, They reign with God their Father, To all e - ter - ni - ty.
one accord they raise Un - to the Lamb that liv - eth An ev - er-last-ing praise.
sing of Thy great love; And at Thy feet a - dore them With all Thy saints above.

CHORUS.

There is joy . . . a - mong the ransomed o - ver there, There is
There is joy,

joy . . . o - ver there; . . . There is joy for - ev - er o - ver there.
There is joy   o - ver there;

J-7

No. 96.   A Lamp Within a Stable.

Margaret E. Sangster.   **Theo. E. Perkins.**

1. No tramp of march-ing ar - mies, No ban-ners flam-ing far;
2. When in the low-ly man-ger The ho - ly moth-er maid
3. No rush of hos - tile ar - mies, But just the hud-dling sheep·

A lamp with-in a sta - ble, And in the sky a star.
In ten-der ad - o - ra - tion Her Babe of Heav-en laid:
Of Christ the an-gels sing - ing, And all the world a - sleep.

Their hymns of peace and glad-ness To earth the an-gels brought;
Born low-ly in the dark-ness, And none so poor as He;
No flame of con-q'ring ban-ners, No le-gions sent a - far;

Their "Glo - ria in Ex - cel - sis" To earth the an-gels taught.
The lit - tle chil-dren of the poor His ver-y own shall be.
A lamp with-in a sta - ble, And in the sky a star.

No. 97. All the Way My Savior Leads Me.

Fanny J. Crosby.

Robert Lowry.

1. All the way my Sav-ior leads me; What have I to ask be-side?
2. All the way my Sav-ior leads me, Cheers each wind-ing path I tread,
3. All the way my Sav-ior leads me; Oh, the full-ness of His love!

Can I doubt His ten-der mer - cy, Who thro' life has been my Guide?
Gives me grace for ev-'ry tri - al, Feeds me with the liv - ing bread.
Per - fect rest to me is prom-ised In my Fa-ther's house a - bove.

Heav'nly peace, di - vin - est com-fort, Here by faith in Him to dwell!
Tho' my wear - y steps may fal - ter, And my soul a-thirst may be,
When my spir - it, clothed im-mor-tal, Wings its flight to realms of day,

For I know, what-e'er be-fall me, Je-sus do-eth all things well; well.
Gush-ing from the Rock be-fore me, Lo! a spring of joy I see; see.
This my song thro' end-less a - ges: Je-sus led me all the way; way.

No. 98.

He is King.

Charlotte G. Homer.   COPYRIGHT, 1910, BY HOPE PUBLISHING CO.   W. Stillman Martin.

1. One there is a-bove all oth-ers we a-dore,—Might-y One of
2. Un-to Him we bow the knee and serv-ice give, And the man-dates
3. When the sea-sons fail, and years neg-lect their flight; When the sun has

Is-ra-el, the King of kings; One whose rule and reign shall be for-
of His ho-ly word ful-fill; In His glo-rious king-dom it is
ceased to shine, and worlds to move; When the moon and stars have fled the

ev-er-more, One whose maj-es-ty all Heav-en sings.
joy to live, Joy to serve Him, joy to do His will.
pale of night, King of kings He yet shall reign in love.

CHORUS.

He is King o-ver the sea and land; His do-min-ion is from

shore to shore; Worlds un-known lie in His might-y

He is King.

hand,   He reigns om - nip - o - tent, and shall for-ev-er - more.

No. 99.   I Would Give My Love.

W. C. Martin.

Florence Williams Falconer.

1. I would give Thee, Lord, the fair-est Of my treasures and the best;
2. Take my heart, for, if Thou take it, Life is sweet and all is well;
3. Keep my heart nor let it wan-der; Let my love grow more and more,—

Something tells my heart Thou car - est More for love than all the rest.
Grief may pain, but can-not break it, Sin may lure, but not com-pel.
Ev - 'ry day find me still fond- er Of the Friend whom I a - dore.

CHORUS.

Let me pour my sweet-est treas-ure On Thy head and on Thy feet:

All my hope and all my pleas-ure In Thy smile are made com-plete.
All my hope   and all my pleasure   In Thy smile are made complete.

No. 100. You May Have the Joy-bells.

J. Edw. Ruark.

Wm. J. Kirkpatrick.

1. You may have the joy-bells ring-ing in your heart, And a peace that
2. Love of Je-sus in its full-ness you may know, And this love to
3. You will meet with tri-als as you jour-ney home, Grace suf-fi-cient
4. Let your life speak well of Je-sus ev-'ry day, Own His right to

from you nev-er will de-part; Walk the straight and nar-row way,
those a-round you sweet-ly show; Words of kind-ness al-ways say,
He will give to o-ver-come; Tho' un-seen by mor-tal eye,
ev-'ry serv-ice you can pay; Sin-ners you can help to win

Live for Je-sus ev-'ry day, He will keep the joy-bells ring-ing in your heart.
Deeds of mercy do each day, Then He'll keep the joy-bells ring-ing in your heart.
He is with you ev-er nigh, And He'll keep the joy-bells ring-ing in your heart.
If your life is pure and clean, And you keep the joy-bells ring-ing in your heart.

FINE.

D. S.—*He will keep the joy-bells ring-ing in your heart.*

Chorus.

Joy - - bells ring-ing in your heart, Joy - - bells
Ring-ing in your heart,   You may have the joy-bells

You May Have the Joy-bells.

ring-ing in your heart; Take the Savior here below, With you ev'rywhere you go;

No. 101.   **Jesus is Calling.**

Fanny J. Crosby.   COPYRIGHT, 1911, BY GEO. C. STEBBINS, RENEWAL.   Geo. C. Stebbins.

1. Je-sus is ten-der-ly call-ing thee home—Call-ing to-day, call-ing to-day;
2. Je-sus is call-ing the wear-y to rest—Call-ing to-day, call-ing to-day;
3. Je-sus is waiting, oh, come to Him now—Waiting to-day, waiting to-day;
4. Je-sus is pleading, oh, list to His voice—Hear Him to-day, hear Him to-day;

Why from the sun-shine of love wilt thou roam Far-ther and far-ther a - way?
Bring Him thy bur-den, and thou shalt be blest; He will not turn Thee a - way.
Come with thy sins, at His feet low-ly bow; Come, and no lon-ger de - lay.
They who be-lieve on His name shall re-joice; Quickly a - rise and a - way.

CHORUS.

Call - ing to - day! Call - ing to - day!
Call - ing, call - ing to - day, to-day! Call - ing, call - ing to - day, to-day!

Je - sus is call - ing, is ten-der-ly call-ing to - day.
Je - sus is ten-der-ly call-ing to - day,

Tell Me the Old. Old Story.

Kate Hankey.   USED BY PERMISSION.   W. H. Doane.

1. Tell me the Old, Old Sto - ry, Of un - seen things a - bove, Of
2. Tell me the sto - ry, slow - ly, That I may take it in— That
3. Tell me the sto - ry soft - ly, With ear - nest tones and grave; Re -
4. Tell me the same old sto - ry, When you have cause to fear That

Je - sus and His glo - ry, Of Je - sus and His love; Tell me the sto - ry
won - der - ful re - demp - tion, God's rem - e - dy for sin; Tell me the sto - ry
mem - ber I'm the sin - ner Whom Je - sus came to save; Tell me the sto - ry
this world's empty glo - ry Is cost - ing me too dear; Yes, and when that world's

sim - ply, As to a lit - tle child, For I am weak and wear - y, And
oft - en, For I for - get so soon, The "ear - ly dew" of morn - ing Has
al - ways, If you would real - ly be, In an - y time of troub - le, A
glo - ry Is dawn - ing on my soul, Tell me the old, old sto - ry: "Christ

CHORUS.

help - less and de - filed.
passed a - way at noon.   Tell me the Old, Old Sto - ry, Tell me the Old, Old
com - fort - er to me.
Je - sus makes thee whole."

Tell Me the Old, Old Story.

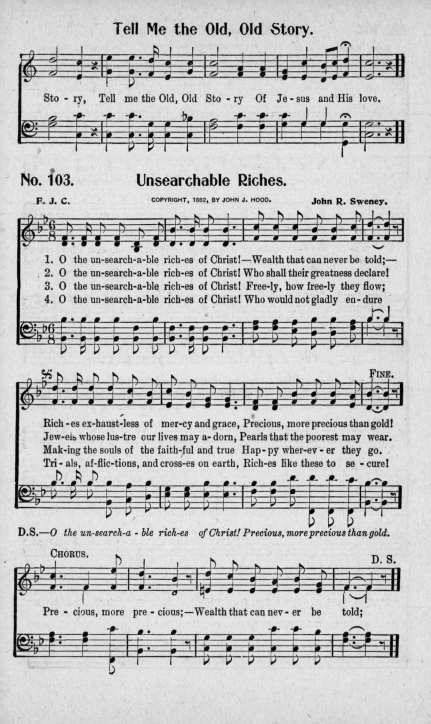

Sto - ry, Tell me the Old, Old Sto - ry Of Je - sus and His love.

No. 103. Unsearchable Riches.

F. J. C.

COPYRIGHT, 1882, BY JOHN J. HOOD.

John R. Sweney.

1. O the un-search-a-ble rich-es of Christ!—Wealth that can never be told;—
2. O the un-search-a-ble rich-es of Christ! Who shall their greatness declare!
3. O the un-search-a-ble rich-es of Christ! Free-ly, how free-ly they flow;
4. O the un-search-a-ble rich-es of Christ! Who would not gladly en-dure

FINE.

Rich-es ex-haust-less of mer-cy and grace, Precious, more precious than gold!
Jew-els whose lus-tre our lives may a-dorn, Pearls that the poorest may wear.
Mak-ing the souls of the faith-ful and true Hap-py wher-ev-er they go.
Tri-als, af-flic-tions, and cross-es on earth, Rich-es like these to se-cure!

D.S.—*O the un-search-a - ble rich-es of Christ! Precious, more precious than gold.*

CHORUS.

D. S.

Pre - cious, more pre - cious;—Wealth that can nev - er be told;

No. 104. The Banner of the Cross.

E. M. Bangs.

Chas. H. Gabriel.

1. Gird on your stead-fast armor, O sol-diers of the cross, Go forward in - to
2. The Gi - ant of Temp-ta-tion Will meet us as we go; We need our strongest
3. The en - e-mies ap-proaching Are Selfishness, and Greed, Vain-glory, and Im-

bat - tle, Nor fear re-pulse nor loss; Make ready for the conflict, The Captain's
ar - mor To greet this mighty foe; But our good sword, Resistance, Will hold and
pa-tience: Our Leader's help we need. Yet ever march-ing onward, Why have we

call o - bey; Then ral-ly and march onward, The trumpet sounds to-day.
bind him fast, And with our Cap-tain lead-ing, We'll conquer him at last.
fear of loss, When o-ver us is float-ing The Ban-ner of the Cross?

CHORUS.

Then onward to the battle, We're marching in our might, We're pressing tow'rd the

vic-to-ry, We're fighting for the right; Upon the breeze resplendent Our col-ors

The Banner of the Cross.

now we toss, And o'er our heads shall ever float The Banner of the Cross.

No. 105.   The Offering.

John J. McLaurin.

COPYRIGHT, 1909, BY E. O. EXCELL.
WORDS AND MUSIC.

E. O. Excell.

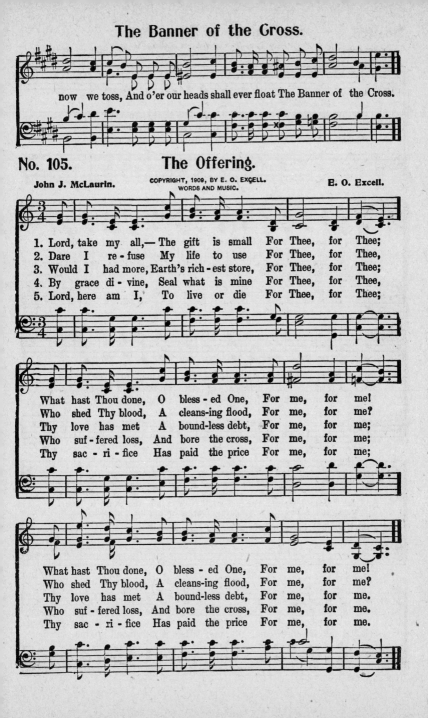

1. Lord, take my all,— The gift is small For Thee, for Thee;
2. Dare I re-fuse My life to use For Thee, for Thee,
3. Would I had more, Earth's rich-est store, For Thee, for Thee;
4. By grace di-vine, Seal what is mine For Thee, for Thee,
5. Lord, here am I, To live or die For Thee, for Thee;

What hast Thou done, O bless-ed One, For me, for me!
Who shed Thy blood, A cleans-ing flood, For me, for me?
Thy love has met A bound-less debt, For me, for me;
Who suf-fered loss, And bore the cross, For me, for me;
Thy sac-ri-fice Has paid the price For me, for me;

What hast Thou done, O bless-ed One, For me, for me!
Who shed Thy blood, A cleans-ing flood, For me, for me?
Thy love has met A bound-less debt, For me, for me.
Who suf-fered loss, And bore the cross, For me, for me.
Thy sac-ri-fice Has paid the price For me, for me.

No. 106. He is All in All to Me.

Mrs. C. H. M.

Mrs. C. H. Morris

1. Long by sin my eyes were blind-ed, And no beau-ty could I see
2. Mil-lions to His feet are com-ing, Just as in the long a-go,
3. Do you won-der that I love Him, When He died my soul to save?

In the wondrous "Man of Sorrows," Who once walked in Gal-i-lee:
When the mul-ti-tudes so thronged Him, Of His wondrous grace to know.
When no price could pay my ran-som, His own pre-cious life He gave!

By His gra-cious touch of heal-ing He has made my eyes to see,
He is still the bur-den-bear-er Of sin-strick-en hu-man kind;
He has won my heart for-ev-er, And my song shall ev-er be,

And the "Man, de-spised, re-ject-ed," Now is all the world to me.
Ad-am's ev-'ry son and daughter May a full de-liv-'rance find.
"Take the world, but give me Je-sus," He is all in all to me.

CHORUS.

He is all in all to me, to me; He is all in all to me, to me;

No. 108. The Hallelujah Song.

COPYRIGHT, 1908, BY WM. J. KIRKPATRICK.
USED BY PERMISSION.

Mrs. C. H. M.

Mrs. C. H. Morris.

1. Let those who've nev-er known our Lord and King Go mourn-ing all the day, go mourn-ing all the day; But we've a song of joy we love to sing While press-ing on our up-ward way.

2. 'Tis heav'n with-in a sin-ner's heart to know His bur-den rolled a-way, his bur-den rolled a-way; His sins like crim-son, made as white as snow, And Christ the Lord come in to stay.

3. The blood, the pre-cious blood of God's dear Son, Is on my soul to-day, is on my soul to-day, And fears and doubt-ings from my heart have flown Since Je-sus washed my sins a-way.

4. Some day be-fore the great white throne we'll sing The hal-le-lu-jah song, the hal-le-lu-jah song Of praise and hon-or to our God and King, With all the ransomed, blood-washed throng.

CHORUS.

Hal-le-lu-jah! for the blood which re-deems us,
re-deems us from all sin,
Hal-le-lu-jah! we'll sing it o'er and o'er;.... Hal-le-lu-jah! for the

The Hallelujah Song.

blood of the bless-ed Son of God, Hal - le - lu - jah for - ev - er more.

No. 109.   'Tis So Sweet to Trust in Jesus.

COPYRIGHT, 1882 AND 1910, BY WM. J. KIRKPATRICK.
USED BY PERMISSION.

Mrs. Louisa M. R. Stead.

Wm. J. Kirkpatrick.

1. 'Tis so sweet to trust in Je - sus, Just to take Him at His Word;
2. O, how sweet to trust in Je - sus, Just to trust His cleansing blood;
3. Yes, 'tis sweet to trust in Je - sus, Just from sin and self to cease;
4. I'm so glad I learned to trust Thee, Precious Je - sus, Sav-ior, Friend;

Just to rest up - on His prom-ise; Just to know, "Thus saith the Lord."
Just in sim - ple faith to plunge me 'Neath the heal - ing, cleansing flood!
Just from Je - sus sim - ply tak - ing Life and rest, and joy and peace.
And I know that Thou art with me, Wilt be with me to the end.

CHORUS.

Je - sus, Je - sus, how I trust Him! How I've proved Him o'er and o'er!

Je - sus, Je - sus, Pre-cious Je - sus! O for grace to trust Him more!

Count Your Blessings.

Rev. J. Oatman, Jr.

E. O. Excell.

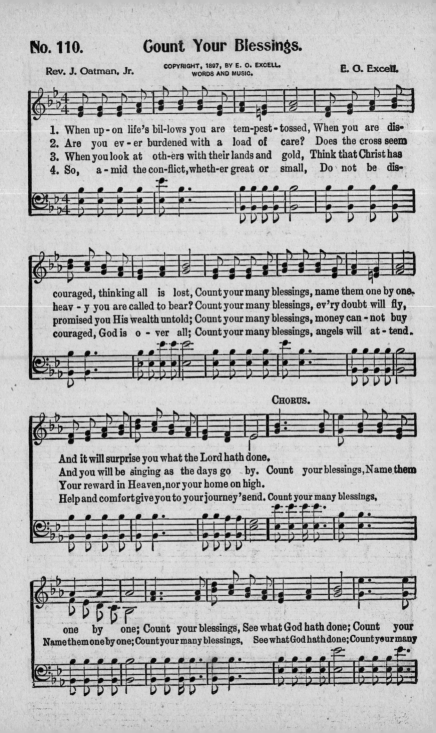

1. When up-on life's bil-lows you are tem-pest-tossed, When you are dis-
2. Are you ev-er burdened with a load of care? Does the cross seem
3. When you look at oth-ers with their lands and gold, Think that Christ has
4. So, a-mid the con-flict, wheth-er great or small, Do not be dis-

couraged, thinking all is lost, Count your many blessings, name them one by one,
heav-y you are called to bear? Count your many blessings, ev'ry doubt will fly,
promised you His wealth untold; Count your many blessings, money can-not buy
couraged, God is o-ver all; Count your many blessings, angels will at-tend.

Chorus.

And it will surprise you what the Lord hath done.
And you will be singing as the days go by. Count your blessings, Name them
Your reward in Heaven, nor your home on high.
Help and comfort give you to your journey's end. Count your many blessings,

one by one; Count your blessings, See what God hath done; Count your
Name them one by one; Count your many blessings, See what God hath done; Count your many

Count Your Blessings.

blessings, Name them one by one; Count your many blessings, See what God hath done.

No. 111.   Somebody.

John R. Clements.

WORDS AND MUSIC COPYRIGHT, 1901, BY W. S. WEEDEN.
E. O. EXCELL, OWNER.

W. S. Weeden.

1. Some-bod-y did a gold-en deed, Proving him-self a friend in need;
2. Some-bod-y tho't 'tis sweet to live, Will-ing-ly said, "I'm glad to give;"
3. Some-bod-y made a lov-ing gift, Cheer-ful-ly tried a load to lift;
4. Some-bod-y i - dled all the hours, Care-less-ly crushed life's fairest flow'rs;
5. Some-bod-y filled the days with light, Constantly chased a - way the night;

Some-bod-y sang a cheer-ful song, Bright'ning the sky the whole day long,—
Some-bod-y fought a val - iant fight, Brave-ly he lived to shield the right,—
Some-bod-y told the love of Christ, Told how His will was sac - ri - ficed,—
Some-bod-y made life loss, not gain, Tho't-less-ly seemed to live in vain,—
Some-bod-y's work bore joy and peace, Sure-ly his life shall nev - er cease,—

Was that some-bod - y you?   Was that some-bod - y you?

J-8

No. 112. If Your Heart Keeps Right.

Rev. Johnson Oatman, Jr.   COPYRIGHT, 1914, BY HAMP SEWELL.   Hamp Sewell.

1. You will live a life of glad-ness if your heart keeps right;
2. You'll go sing-ing on life's path-way if your heart keeps right,
3. You will al-ways be a bless-ing if your heart keeps right,

Tho' your foes may gather and your friends may slight, You may find a Friend who's
Tho' the clouds may deepen in-to shades of night; For, tho' night may do for
Then the Master's serv-ice will be your delight, And you nev-er will be

faith-ful and who al-ways conquers; He will help you if your heart keeps right.
weep-ing, joy will come with morning, Bringing sunshine if your heart keeps right.
lone-ly for the Lord hath spo-ken, "I'll be with you if your heart keeps right."

CHORUS.

If your heart keeps right, if your heart keeps right, Ev-'ry cloud will change to

sunshine, darkness turn to light; You'll have gladness on your way and a

If Your Heart Keeps Right.

bless-ing ev - 'ry day   If   the Sav-ior helps you and your heart keeps right.

No. 113.   Lord, I'm Coming Home.

W. J. K.   COPYRIGHT, 1892, BY WM. J. KIRKPATRICK.
USED BY PERMISSION.   Wm. J. Kirkpatrick.

1. I've wan-dered far   a - way from God, Now I'm com-ing home;
2. I've wast - ed man - y   pre - cious years, Now I'm com-ing home;
3. I've tired of sin and   stray-ing, Lord, Now I'm com-ing home;
4. My soul is sick, my heart is sore, Now I'm com-ing home;

Fine.

The paths of sin too long I've trod, Lord, I'm com-ing home.
I now re - pent with bit - ter tears, Lord, I'm com-ing home.
I'll trust Thy love, be - lieve Thy word, Lord, I'm com-ing home.
My strength re - new, my hope re - store, Lord, I'm com-ing home.

D. S.—*O - pen wide Thine arms of love, Lord, I'm com-ing home.*

Chorus.   **D. S.**

Com - ing home, com - ing home, Nev - er - more to roam,

5 My only hope, my only plea,
   Now I'm coming home;
That Jesus died, and died for me,
   Lord, I'm coming home.

6 I need His cleansing blood, I know,
   Now I'm coming home;
O wash me whiter than the snow,
   Lord, I'm coming home.

No. 114.   More Like the Master.

C. H. G.

Chas. H. Gabriel.

1. More like the Mas-ter I would ev-er be, More of His meekness,
more hu-mil - i - ty; More zeal to la-bor, more courage to be
true, More con-se-cra-tion for work He bids me do.

2. More like the Mas-ter, is my dai-ly prayer; More strength to car-ry
cross-es I must bear; More ear-nest ef-fort to bring His king-dom
in; More of His Spir-it, the wan-der-er to win.

3. More like the Mas-ter I would live and grow; More of His love to
oth-ers I would show; More self-de-ni-al, like His in Gal-i-
lee, More like the Mas-ter I long to ev-er be.

rit.

CHORUS.

Take Thou my heart,— I would be Thine a-lone;.. Take Thou my
Take my heart, O take my heart, I would be Thine a-lone; Take my heart, O

heart.. and make it all Thine own;.... Purge me from sin,.... O
take my heart and make it all Thine own; Purge Thou me from ev'ry sin, O

More Like the Master.

Lord, I now im-plore, Wash me and keep me Thine for-ev-er-more.

Lord, I now im-plore, Wash and keep, O wash and keep me Thine for-ev-er-more.

No. 115.

What Did He Do?

Dr. J. M. Gray.

W. Owen.

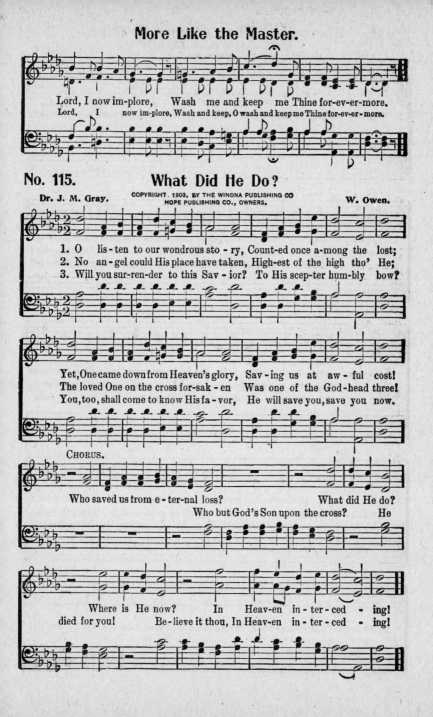

1. O lis-ten to our wondrous sto-ry, Count-ed once a-mong the lost;
2. No an-gel could His place have taken, High-est of the high tho' He;
3. Will you sur-ren-der to this Sav-ior? To His scep-ter hum-bly bow?

Yet, One came down from Heaven's glory, Sav-ing us at aw-ful cost!
The loved One on the cross for-sak-en Was one of the God-head three!
You, too, shall come to know His fa-vor, He will save you, save you now.

CHORUS.

Who saved us from e-ter-nal loss? What did He do?
Who but God's Son upon the cross? He

Where is He now? In Heav-en in-ter-ced - ing!
died for you! Be-lieve it thou, In Heav-en in-ter-ced - ing!

No. 116. Where Hast Thou Gleaned To-Day?

P. P. Bliss.

P. P. Bliss.

Question.

1. Wear - y glean-er, whence comest thou, With emp-ty hands and cloud-ed brow?
2. Care - less glean-er, what hast thou here, These fad-ed flow'rs and leaf-lets sere?
3. Bur-dened glean-er, thy sheaves I see; In - deed thou must a - wear - y be!

Plod-ding a - long thy lone - ly way, Tell me, where hast thou gleaned to-day?
Hun-gry and thirst-y, tell me, pray, Where, oh, where hast thou gleaned to-day?
Sing-ing a - long the homeward way, Glad one, where hast thou gleaned to-day?

Answer.

Late I found a bar - ren field, The har - vest past, my search re-vealed
All day long in sha - dy bow'rs, I've gai - ly sought earth's fairest flow'rs;
Stay me not, till day is done I've gath-ered hand-fuls one by one;

Oth - ers gold - en sheaves had gained, On - ly stub - ble for me re-mained.
Now, a - las! too late I see All I've gath-ered is van - i - ty.
Here and there for me they fall, Close by the reapers I've found them all.

CHORUS.

Forth to the har - vest - field a - way! Gath-er your hand-fuls while you may;

Where Hast Thou Gleaned To-day?

All day long in the field a - bide. Glean-ing close by the reap - er's side.

No. 117.   Look and Live.

W. A. O.

COPYRIGHT, 1915, BY E. O. EXCELL. RENEWAL.
WORDS AND MUSIC.

W. A. Ogden.

1. I've a message from the Lord, Hal-le-lu-jah! The message un-to you I'll give;
2. I've a message full of love, Hal-le-lu-jah! A message, O my friend, for you;
3. Life is of-fered un - to you, Hal-le-lu-jah! E - ter-nal life thy soul shall have,
4. I will tell you how I came, Hal-le-lu-jah! To Jesus when He made me whole:

FINE.

'T is re-cord-ed in His word, Hal-le - lu - jah! It is on-ly that you "look and live."
'T is a message from above, Hal-le - lu - jah! Je-sus said it, and I know 'tis true.
If you'll on-ly look to Him, Hal-le - lu - jah! Look to Jesus, who a-lone can save.
'T was believing on His name, Hal-le - lu - jah! I trusted, and He saved my soul.

D. S.–'T is recorded in His word, Hal-le-lu-jah! It is on - ly that you "look and live."

CHORUS.

D. S.

"Look and live,"......my brother, live,   Look to Je - sus now and live;
"Look and live," my brother, live, "Look and live,"

My Savior First of All.

Fanny J. Crosby.

Jno. R. Sweney.

1. When my life-work is end-ed and I cross the swelling tide, When the
2. O, the soul-thrill-ing rapture when I view His bless-ed face, And the
3. O, the dear ones in glo-ry, how they beck-on me to come, And our
4. Thro' the gates to the cit-y, in a robe of spot-less white He will

bright and glorious morning I shall see, I shall know my Redeemer when I
lus-ter of His kind-ly beaming eye; How my full heart will praise Him for the
part-ing at the riv-er I re-call; To the sweet vales of E-den they will
lead me where no tears will ev-er fall; In the glad song of a-ges I shall

reach the oth-er side, And His smile will be the first to welcome me.
mer-cy, love and grace, That prepare for me a man-sion in the sky.
sing my welcome home; But I long to meet my Sav-ior first of all.
min-gle with de-light; But I long to meet my Sav-ior first of all.

CHORUS.

I shall know Him, I shall know Him, And redeemed by His side I shall stand;
I shall know Him,

My Savior First of All.

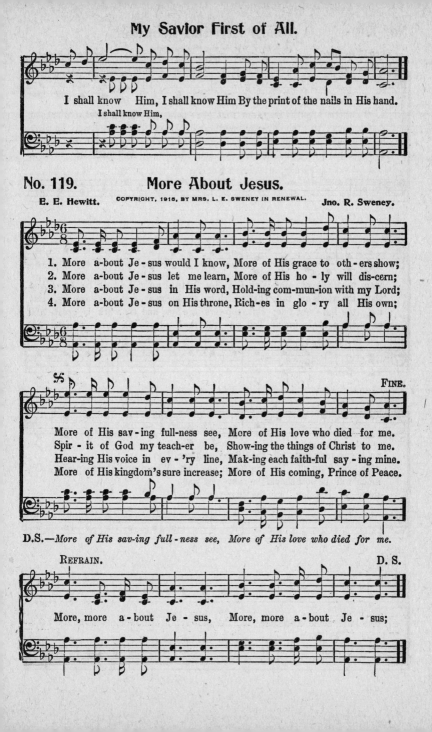

I shall know Him, I shall know Him By the print of the nails in His hand.

I shall know Him,

No. 119.　More About Jesus.

E. E. Hewitt.　COPYRIGHT, 1915, BY MRS. L. E. SWENEY IN RENEWAL.　Jno. R. Sweney.

1. More a-bout Je - sus would I know, More of His grace to oth - ers show;
2. More a-bout Je - sus let me learn, More of His ho - ly will dis-cern;
3. More a-bout Je - sus in His word, Hold-ing com-mun-ion with my Lord;
4. More a-bout Je - sus on His throne, Rich-es in glo - ry all His own;

Fine.

More of His sav-ing full-ness see, More of His love who died for me.
Spir - it of God my teach-er be, Show-ing the things of Christ to me.
Hear-ing His voice in ev - 'ry line, Mak-ing each faith-ful say - ing mine.
More of His kingdom's sure increase; More of His coming, Prince of Peace.

D.S.—*More of His sav-ing full-ness see, More of His love who died for me.*

REFRAIN.　　　　　　　　　　　　　　　　　**D. S.**

More, more a - bout Je - sus, More, more a - bout Je - sus;

No. 120. O Where Are the Reapers?

Eben E. Rexford.

George F. Root.

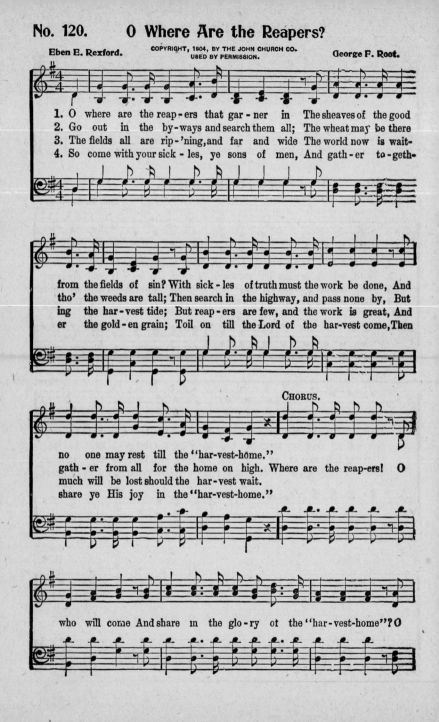

1. O where are the reap-ers that gar-ner in The sheaves of the good from the fields of sin? With sick-les of truth must the work be done, And no one may rest till the "har-vest-home."

2. Go out in the by-ways and search them all; The wheat may be there tho' the weeds are tall; Then search in the highway, and pass none by, But gath-er from all for the home on high. Where are the reap-ers! O who will come And share in the glo-ry of the "har-vest-home"? O

3. The fields all are rip-'ning, and far and wide The world now is wait-ing the har-vest tide; But reap-ers are few, and the work is great, And much will be lost should the har-vest wait.

4. So come with your sick-les, ye sons of men, And gath-er to-geth-er the gold-en grain; Toil on till the Lord of the har-vest come, Then share ye His joy in the "har-vest-home."

CHORUS.

Where are the reap-ers! O who will come And share in the glo-ry of the "har-vest-home"? O

O Where Are the Reapers?

who will help us to gar-ner in The sheaves of good from the fields of sin?

No. 121. Wonderful Words of Life.

P. P. B.

P. P. Bliss.

1. Sing them o-ver a-gain to me, Won-der-ful words of Life;
2. Christ, the bless-ed One, gives to all, Won-der-ful words of Life;
3. Sweet-ly ech-o the gos-pel call, Won-der-ful words of Life;

Let me more of their beau-ty see, Won-der-ful words of Life.
Sin-ner, list to the lov-ing call, Won-der-ful words of Life.
Of-fer par-don and peace to all, Won-der-ful words of Life.

Words of life and beau-ty, Teach me faith and du-ty:
All so free-ly giv-en, Woo-ing us to Heav-en:
Je-sus, on-ly Sav-ior, Sanc-ti-fy for-ev-er:

Refrain.

Beau-ti-ful words, beau-ti-ful words, Wonderful words of Life; Life.

Over and Over Again.

Floy S. Armstrong.

Chas. H. Gabriel.

1. How man-y times has He lightened our cares, O-ver and o-ver a-gain! How
2. He ne'er re-fus-es to hear, tho' we call O-ver and o-ver a-gain, Sends
3. Tho' we may wander in by-ways of sin, O-ver and o-ver a-gain, The

many times has He answered our prayers, Over and over a-gain! Then tell of His
show'rs of blessings so freely on all, O-ver and o-ver a-gain; Oh, why are you
heart of Je-sus will bid us come in, O-ver and o-ver a-gain; Then let us be

good-ness to thee and to thine, And tell of His mercies to me and to mine. Re-
si - lent so often, so long, When telling the story will turn them from wrong? Then
will - ing, wher-ev-er the place, To tell of His kindness, His pardon, His grace, And

peat the old sto-ry of par-don di-vine, O-ver and o-ver a-gain. . . . .
tell it, O tell it in praise or in song,
some day in glory we'll look on His face, o . . . ver and o-ver a-gain.

CHORUS.

O-ver and o-ver a-gain, . . . O-ver and o-ver a-gain, ...
and o-ver a-gain, and o-ver a-gain

Over And Over Again.

O what a won-der-ful sto-ry to tell, O - ver and o - ver a - gain.

No. 123.

Lead Me, Savior.

FROM "CAROLS OF JOY."
USED BY PERMISSION OF JOHN J. HOOD.

F. M. D.

Frank M. Davis.

1. Sav-ior, lead me, lest I stray,　Gen-tly lead me all the way;
2. Thou the ref-uge of my soul　When life's stormy billows roll;
3. Sav-ior, lead me, then at last,　When the storm of life is past,

1. Sav - ior,　lead me, lest I stray, Gen - tly　lead me all the way;

I am safe when by Thy side,　I would in Thy love a - bide.
I am safe when Thou art nigh,　All my hopes on Thee re-ly.
To the land of end-less day,　Where all tears are wiped a-way.

I　am　safe when by Thy side, I　would　in Thy love abide.

Chorus.

Lead me, lead me, Sav - ior, lead me, lest I stray; ....

lest I stray;

Gen-tly down the stream of time,　Lead me, Sav-ior, all the way.

stream of time,

all the way.

No. 124. Follow Me.

O. M. Bills.

M. L. McPhail.

1. Like a chime of sil - ver bells In the darkness ring-ing, Comes a voice that
2. Lost one, will you close your ears To the mag - ic sto - ry That can charm a-
3. Lo! the tempter doth de-ceive, Lur-ing you to sad-ness; Then he mocks you

ev - er tells Of the Shepherd's care; To the wan-d'rer from the fold,
way your fears When earth's joys de - part? Shall the spell of e - vil hide
while you grieve, Pointing to de - spair; From his fet - ters break a - way,

Love is ev - er bring-ing Tidings from the gates of gold, Of a wel-come there.
From your eyes the glo-ry That for-ev - er will a - bide With the pure in heart?
Seek the path of glad-ness, Spurn the pleasures that decay, Of their sting beware.

CHORUS.

"Fol - low Me," O hear the Shepherd say - ing, "Seek the
"Fol - low, fol - low, fol - low Me," "Seek the door to

door to pas-tures ev - er fair;" Heed, O heed thy
pas - tures fair, to pas - tures ev - er fair;" Heed, O heed thy Sav - ior's voice, O

Follow Me.

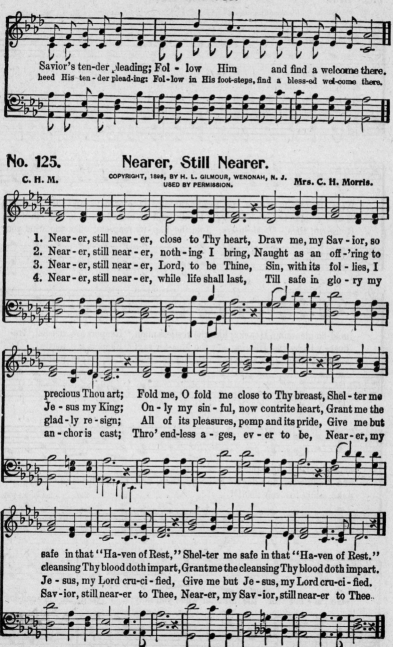

Savior's ten-der pleading; Fol - low Him and find a welcome there.
heed His ten-der plead-ing: Fol-low in His foot-steps, find a bless-ed wel-come there.

No. 125. Nearer, Still Nearer.

C. H. M.

Mrs. C. H. Morris.

1. Near-er, still near-er, close to Thy heart, Draw me, my Sav-ior, so
2. Near-er, still near-er, noth-ing I bring, Naught as an off-'ring to
3. Near-er, still near-er, Lord, to be Thine, Sin, with its fol-lies, I
4. Near-er, still near-er, while life shall last, Till safe in glo-ry my

precious Thou art; Fold me, O fold me close to Thy breast, Shel-ter me
Je - sus my King; On - ly my sin-ful, now contrite heart, Grant me the
glad - ly re-sign; All of its pleasures, pomp and its pride, Give me but
an - chor is cast; Thro' end-less a - ges, ev - er to be, Near-er, my

safe in that "Ha-ven of Rest," Shel-ter me safe in that "Ha-ven of Rest."
cleansing Thy blood doth impart, Grant me the cleansing Thy blood doth impart.
Je - sus, my Lord cru-ci-fied, Give me but Je - sus, my Lord cru-ci-fied.
Sav-ior, still near-er to Thee, Near-er, my Sav-ior, still near-er to Thee.

No. 126.   Harvest Song!

C. H. G.   Chas. H. Gabriel.

WORDS AND MUSIC COPYRIGHT, 1907, BY CHAS. H. GABRIEL.
E. O. EXCELL, OWNER.

1. Look, the har-vest-field is teem-ing With the rich and ri-pened grain;
2. In the mar-kets and the by-ways, Whil-ing pre-cious hours a-way,
3. Hear ye not the faith-ful sing-ing Of the la-bor and the yield?

Wide it spreads be-fore us, Bright the sky is o'er us; In the sun-light,
Man-y stand com-plain-ing, I-dle still re-main-ing, Loit'ring in the
Rouse ye, then, O sleep-ers, Join the hap-py reap-ers; To the wind your

gold-en gleaming, Heaving like the restless main, "Reapers are needed," re-
dust-y highways, Hearing not the Mas-ter say: "Reapers are needed, O
sor-rows flinging, Pa-tient-ly the sick-le wield: "Reapers are needed, A-

CHORUS.

sounds o'er hill and plain.
who will work to-day?" Rouse ye, then, and to the fields a-way,
wake, and to the field!"   to the fields a-way.

Go la-bor for the Mas-ter while you may;   Lo! He is call-ing,
                    Mas - - ter   while you may;

Harvest Song.

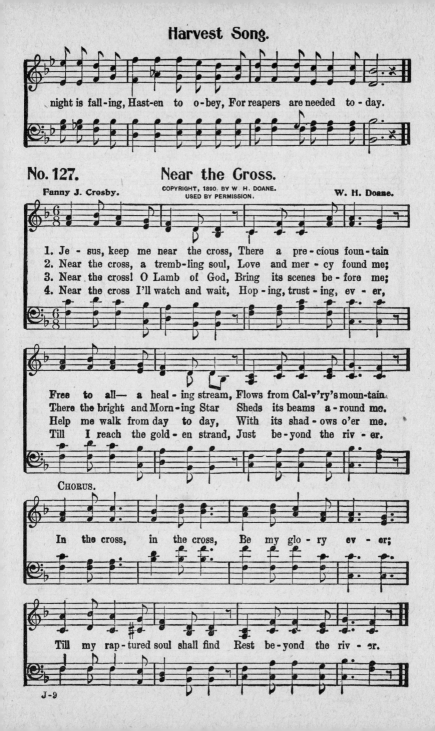

night is fall-ing, Hast-en to o-bey, For reapers are needed to-day.

No. 127. Near the Cross.

Fanny J. Crosby.

W. H. Doane.

1. Je - sus, keep me near the cross, There a pre-cious foun-tain
2. Near the cross, a tremb-ling soul, Love and mer - cy found me;
3. Near the cross! O Lamb of God, Bring its scenes be - fore me;
4. Near the cross I'll watch and wait, Hop - ing, trust - ing, ev - er,

Free to all— a heal - ing stream, Flows from Cal-v'ry's moun-tain.
There the bright and Morn-ing Star Sheds its beams a - round me.
Help me walk from day to day, With its shad - ows o'er me.
Till I reach the gold - en strand, Just be-yond the riv - er.

CHORUS.

In the cross, in the cross, Be my glo-ry ev - er;

Till my rap-tured soul shall find Rest be-yond the riv - er.

No. 128. Willing Am I.

E. D. E.

Wm. Edie Marks.

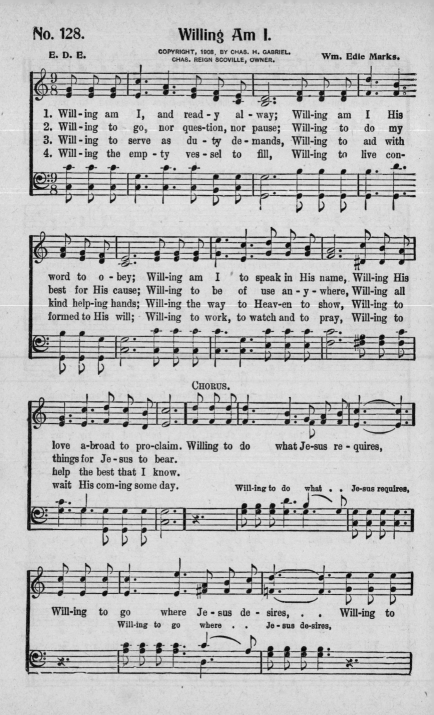

1. Will-ing am I, and read-y al-way; Will-ing am I His
2. Will-ing to go, nor ques-tion, nor pause; Will-ing to do my
3. Will-ing to serve as du-ty de-mands, Will-ing to aid with
4. Will-ing the emp-ty ves-sel to fill, Will-ing to live con-

word to o-bey; Will-ing am I to speak in His name, Will-ing His
best for His cause; Will-ing to be of use an-y-where, Will-ing all
kind help-ing hands; Will-ing the way to Heav-en to show, Will-ing to
formed to His will; Will-ing to work, to watch and to pray, Will-ing to

Chorus.

love a-broad to pro-claim. Willing to do what Je-sus re-quires,
things for Je-sus to bear.
help the best that I know.
wait His com-ing some day.

Will-ing to do what . . Je-sus requires,

Will-ing to go where Je-sus de-sires, . . Will-ing to

Will-ing to go where . . Je-sus de-sires,

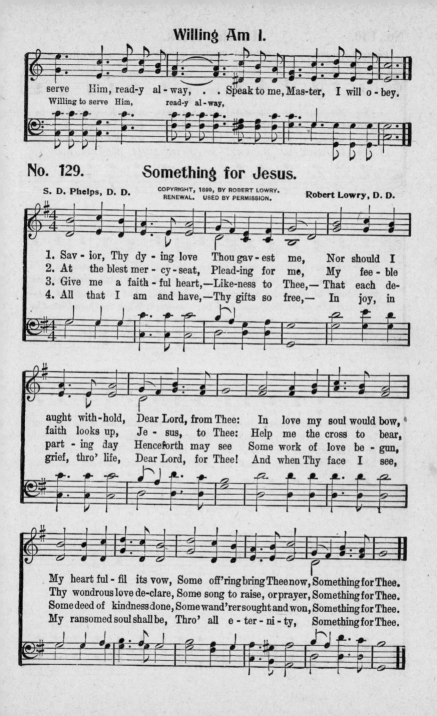

No. 130. To the Work.

Fanny J. Crosby. COPYRIGHT, 1899, BY W. H. DOANE. W. H. Doane.

1. To the work! to the work! we are serv-ants of God, Let us fol-low the path that our Mas-ter has trod; With the balm of His coun-sel our strength to re-new, Let us do with our might what our hands find to do. Toil-ing on, toil-ing on,

2. To the work! to the work! let the hun-gry be fed; To the foun-tain of life let the wear-y be led; In the cross and its ban-ner our glo-ry shall be, While we her-ald the ti-dings, "Sal-va-tion is free!"

3. To the work! to the work! there is la-bor for all; For the king-dom of dark-ness and er-ror shall fall; And the name of Je-ho-vah ex-alt-ed shall be, In the loud-swell-ing cho-rus, "Sal-va-tion is free!"

4. To the work' to the work! in the strength of the Lord, And a robe and a crown shall our la-bor re-ward; When the home of the faith-ful our dwell-ing shall be, And we shout with the ransomed, "Sal-va-tion is free!"

CHORUS.

Toil-ing on, toil-ing on,

To the Work.

Toil - ing on,   toil - ing on;   Let us hope,
Toil - ing on,   toil - ing on;   and trust,

let us watch,   And la - bor till the Mas - ter comes.
and pray,

No. 131.   **I Am Coming, Lord.**

L. H.   Rev. L. Hartsough.

1. I hear Thy wel-come voice, That calls me, Lord, to Thee, For
2. Tho' com-ing weak and vile, Thou dost my strength as-sure; Thou
3. 'Tis Je - sus calls me on   To per-fect faith and love, To

FINE.

cleans-ing in Thy pre-cious blood That flowed on Cal - va - ry.
dost my vile-ness full - y cleanse, Till spot - less all and pure.
per - fect hope, and peace, and trust, For earth and heav'n a - bove.

D. S.--That flowed on Cal - va - ry!

CHORUS.   D. S.

I am coming, Lord! Com-ing now to Thee! Wash me, cleanse me, in the blood

No. 132. The Fight Is On.

Mrs. C. H. M. COPYRIGHT, 1905, BY WM. J. KIRKPATRICK. Mrs. C. H. Morris.

1. The fight is on, the trump-et sound is ring-ing out, The
2. The fight is on, a-rouse, ye sol-diers brave and true! Je-
3. The Lord is lead-ing on to cer-tain vic-to-ry; The

cry "To arms!" is heard a-far and near; The Lord of hosts is
ho-vah leads, and vic-t'ry will as-sure; Go, buck-le on the
bow of prom-ise spans the east-ern sky; His glo-rious name in

march-ing on to vic-to-ry, The tri-umph of the Christ will soon ap-pear.
ar-mor God has giv-en you, And in His strength un-to the end en-dure.
ev-'ry land shall honored be; The morn will break, the dawn of peace is nigh.

CHORUS. *Unison.*

The fight is on, O Christian sol-dier, And face to face in stern ar-ray, With ar-mor

Harmony.

gleaming, and colors streaming, The right and wrong engage to-day! The fight is

The Fight Is On.

on, but be not wear-y; Be strong, and in His might hold fast; If God be

for us, His ban-ner o'er us, We'll sing the vic-tor's song at last!
Vic-t'ry, Vic-t'ry.

No. 133. ## More Love to Thee.

Elizabeth Prentiss. USED BY PERMISSION. W. H. Doane.

1. More love to Thee, O Christ, More love to Thee! Hear Thou the
2. Once earth-ly joy I craved, Sought peace and rest; Now Thee a-
3. Then shall my lat-est breath Whis-per Thy praise; This be the

prayer I make On bend-ed knee; This is my ear-nest plea:
lone I seek, Give what is best; This all my prayer shall be:
part-ing cry My heart shall raise; This still its prayer shall be:

More love, O Christ, to Thee, More love to Thee, More love to Thee!

No. 134. Saved! Saved!

J. P. S. COPYRIGHT, 1911, BY ROBERT H. COLEMAN. J. P. Scholfield.

1. I've found a Friend who is all to me,.... His
2. He saves me from ev-'ry sin and harm,.. Se-
3. When poor and need-y, and all a-lone,... In

love is ev-er true:............ I love to tell.. how He
cures my soul each day;............. I'm lean-ing strong on His
love He said to me,............ "Come un-to Me... and I'll

lift-ed me, ...And what His grace can do for you....
might-y arm;.. I know He'll guide me all the way...
lead you home,.. To live with Me e-ter-nal-ly."...

Saved! Saved!

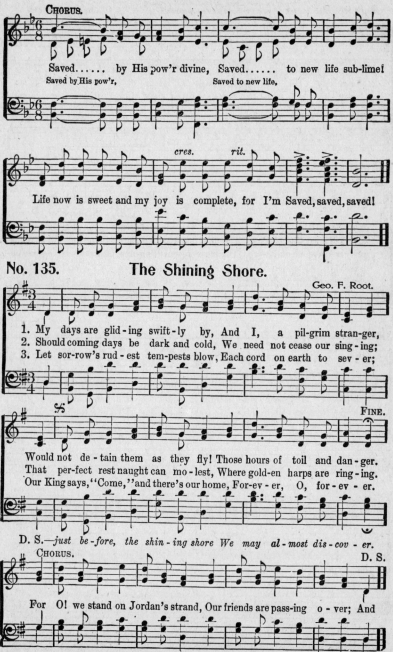

CHORUS.

Saved...... by His pow'r divine, Saved...... to new life sub-lime!

Saved by His pow'r,   Saved to new life,

cres.   *rit.*

Life now is sweet and my joy is complete, for I'm Saved, saved, saved!

No. 135.   ## The Shining Shore.

Geo. F. Root.

1. My days are glid-ing swift-ly by, And I, a pil-grim stran-ger,
2. Should coming days be dark and cold, We need not cease our sing-ing;
3. Let sor-row's rud-est tem-pests blow, Each cord on earth to sev-er;

FINE.

Would not de-tain them as they fly! Those hours of toil and dan-ger.
That per-fect rest naught can mo-lest, Where gold-en harps are ring-ing.
Our King says, "Come," and there's our home, For-ev-er, O, for-ev-er.

D. S.—*just be-fore, the shin-ing shore We may al-most dis-cov-er.*

CHORUS.   **D. S.**

For O! we stand on Jordan's strand, Our friends are pass-ing o-ver; And

No. 136. Some Day.

Dr. Victor M. Staley. Chas. H. Gabriel.

1. Some day 'twill all be o - ver—The toil and cares of life; Some
2. Some day I'll see the man-sions Of Heav - en's cit - y fair; Some
3. Some day I'll see the Sav - ior, And know Him, face to face; Some

day the world be vanquished, With all this mor-tal strife; Some day, the journey
day I'll greet with pleasure, The dear ones waiting there; Some day I'll hear the
day re-ceive, un-meas-ured, The bless-ings of His grace; Some day He'll smile up-

end-ed, I'll lay my bur-den down; Some day, in realms su - per-nal Re-
voi-ces Of God's an - gel-ic throng; Some day I'll join the cho-rus In
on me from that white throne a-bove; Some day I'll know the full-ness Of

Chorus.

ceive; at last, my crown.
Heav'n's im-mor-tal song. Some day, . . . some happy day. . . .
His un - dy-ing love. some hap-py day, some hap-py day,

Some Day.

The Lord will wipe all tears a - way, . . . And I shall go to dwell with
all tears a - way,

Him, . . . To dwell with Him . . . . some hap-py day.
to dwell with Him,   To dwell with Him some hap-py, hap-py day.

No. 137.   Room At the Cross.

W. B. B.   Wm. B. Blake.

1. Room at the cross for a trem - bling soul, Room at the cross for you;
2. Room at the cross for a break - ing heart, Room at the cross for you;
3. Room at the cross for earth's weary and worn, Room at the cross for you;

Where the sin - lad - en may be made whole, Room at the cross for you.
Choose, then, like Ma - ry, the bet - ter part; Room at the cross for you.
Come, then, O has - ten, ye souls who mourn, Room at the cross for you.

REFRAIN.   1   2

Room, room, room at the cross, Room at the cross for you;
Room, room, room at the cross, [Omit . . . .] Room at the cross for you.

No. 138. Why Stand Ye Here Idle?

J. L. McDonald.   E. O. Excell.

1. Why stand ye here i - dle? there's la - bor for all, The vine - yard needs
2. Why stand ye here i - dle? a bro - ther's in need, His cries as - cend
3. Why stand ye here i - dle? a soul's be - ing lost, Speak, speak words of
4. Why stand ye here i - dle? O la - bor each day, To lead men to

work - men, the weeds are grown tall; The ripe fruit is wast - ing for
heav'n - ward, then pray you, give heed; For food and for rai - ment he
warn - ing, what - ev - er the cost; The soul you may res - cue from
Je - sus, the Truth, Life and Way; The Spir - it has promised its

lack of strong hands, Why stand ye here i - dle? the Mas - ter de - mands.
suf - fers to - night, Then ren - der as - sist - ance; O, dare to do right.
sin and from shame, And give to the Sav - ior to praise His dear name.
pres - ence to lend, To com - fort and strengthen, till la - bors shall end.

CHORUS.

Oh, { why . . . . stand ye i - dle, ... Oh, why . . . . stand ye
     { har - - - vest is pass - ing, ... The har - - - vest is

Oh, { why stand ye i - dle, so i - dle all day? Oh, why stand ye i - dle, so
     { har - vest is pass - ing, is pass - ing a - way, The har - vest is pass - ing, is

Why Stand Ye Here Idle?

i - dle,...... Oh, why.......... stand ye i - dle,.......
pass - ing,...... The har - - - vest is pass - ing,......
i - dle all day? Oh, why stand ye i - dle, so i - dle all day,
pass-ing a - way, The har - vest is pass - ing, is pass - ing a - way.

rit.

i - - - dle all day?..... The pass - - ing a - way.
i - dle all day, i - dle all day? The pass-ing a-way, passing a - way.

No. 139. No Dying There.

F. A. B.

F. A. Blackmer.

1. A land by faith I see, Where saints shall ever be Free from mor-tal-i-ty,
2. There friends shall meet again, In happiness to reign, While thro' that blest domain,
3. There sorrow cannot stay; There tears are wiped away, One bright e-ter-nal day,

D. S.—*In that fair, heav'nly land,*

Fine. Refrain. D.S.

No dy-ing there. No dy-ing there,........ No dy-ing there;........
No dy-ing there. No dy-ing there, No dy-ing there;

No. 140.   What Shall the Harvest Be?

Mrs. Emily S. Oakley.

P. P. Bliss.

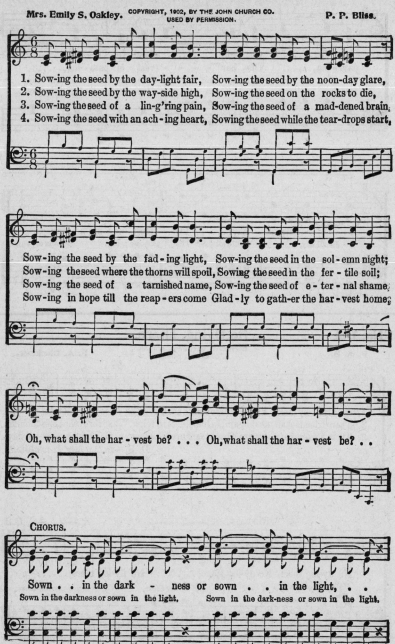

1. Sow-ing the seed by the day-light fair, Sow-ing the seed by the noon-day glare,
2. Sow-ing the seed by the way-side high, Sow-ing the seed on the rocks to die,
3. Sow-ing the seed of a lin-g'ring pain, Sow-ing the seed of a mad-dened brain,
4. Sow-ing the seed with an ach-ing heart, Sowing the seed while the tear-drops start,

Sow-ing the seed by the fad-ing light, Sow-ing the seed in the sol-emn night;
Sow-ing the seed where the thorns will spoil, Sowing the seed in the fer-tile soil;
Sow-ing the seed of a tarnished name, Sow-ing the seed of e-ter-nal shame;
Sow-ing in hope till the reap-ers come Glad-ly to gath-er the har-vest home;

Oh, what shall the har-vest be? . . . Oh, what shall the har-vest be? . .

Chorus.

Sown . . in the dark-ness or sown . . in the light, . . .

Sown in the darkness or sown in the light, Sown in the dark-ness or sown in the light,

What Shall the Harvest Be?

Sown .. in our weak-ness or sown .. in our might, Gath-ered in

Sown in our weakness or sown in our might, Sown in our weakness or sown in our might, Gathered in

time or e-ter-ni-ty, Sure, ah, sure will the har-vest be...

time or e-ter-ni-ty, Sure, ah, sure will the har-vest, har-vest be.

No. 141. My Shepherd is the Lord.

Anon. Virgil C. Taylor.

1. My Shep-herd is the Lord Most High, And all my wants shall be sup-plied:
2. He in His mer-cy doth re-store My soul when sink-ing in dis-tress;
3. Yea, tho' I walk thro' death's dark vale, E'en there no e-vil will I fear,
4. For me a ta-ble Thou hast spread, Prepared be-fore the face of foes;

In pas-tures green He makes me lie, And leads by streams which gently glide.
For His name's sake He ev-er-more Leads me in paths of right-eous-ness.
Be-cause Thy presence shall not fail, Thy rod and staff my soul shall cheer.
With oil Thou dost a-noint my head: My cup is filled and o-ver-flows.

Awake! Awake!

Fanny J. Crosby.

John R. Sweney.

1. A - wake! a - wake! the Mas-ter now is call-ing us, A - rise! a-
2. A cry for light from dy - ing ones in heathen lands; It comes, it
3. O Church of God, ex-tend thy kind, ma-ter - nal arms To save the
4. Look up! look up! the prom-ised day is draw-ing near, When all shall

rise! and, trust-ing in His word, Go forth! go forth! pro-claim the year of
comes a - cross the ocean's foam; Then haste! oh, haste to spread the words of
lost on mountains dark and cold; Reach out thy hand with lov - ing smile to
hail, shall hail the Sav - ior King; When peace and joy shall fold their wings in

ju - bi - lee, And take the cross, the bless-ed cross of Christ our Lord.
truth a-broad, For-get - ting not the starving poor at home, dear home.
res - cue them, And bring them to the shel - ter of the Sav - ior's fold.
ev - 'ry clime, And "Glo - ry, hal - le - lu - jah!" o'er the earth shall ring.

CHORUS.

On, on, swell the cho - rus; On, on, the morning star is shin-ing o'er us;
On, on, on, swell the cho-rus; On, on, on,

Awake! Awake!

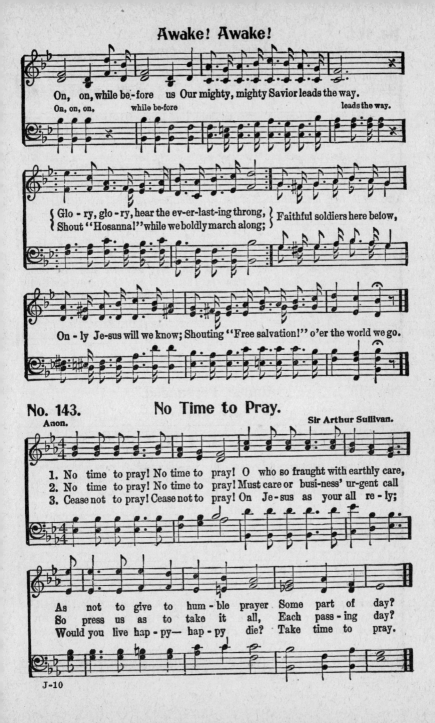

On, on, while be-fore us Our mighty, mighty Savior leads the way.

On, on, on, while be-fore   leads the way.

Glo - ry, glo - ry, hear the ev-er-last-ing throng,
Shout "Hosanna!" while we boldly march along; } Faithful soldiers here below,

On - ly Je-sus will we know; Shouting "Free salvation!" o'er the world we go.

No. 143.   No Time to Pray.

Anon.   Sir Arthur Sullivan.

1. No time to pray! No time to pray! O who so fraught with earthly care,
2. No time to pray! No time to pray! Must care or busi-ness' ur-gent call
3. Cease not to pray! Cease not to pray! On Je-sus as your all re - ly;

As   not   to give   to hum - ble prayer Some   part   of   day?
So   press   us   as   to take   it   all,   Each   pass - ing day?
Would you live hap - py— hap - py die? Take   time   to   pray.

No. 144.
I'll Live For Him.

R. E. Hudson.

C. R. Dunbar.

1. My life, my love I give to Thee, Thou Lamb of God who died for me;
2. I now be-lieve Thou dost re-ceive, For Thou hast died that I might live;
3. O Thou who died on Cal-va-ry, To save my soul and make me free,

CHO.—I'll live for Him who died for me, How hap-py then my life shall be!

D. C. Chorus.

Oh, may I ev-er faith-ful be, My Sav-ior and my God!
And now hence-forth I'll trust in Thee, My Sav-ior and my God!
I'll con-se-crate my life to Thee, My Sav-ior and my God!

I'll live for Him who died for me, My Sav-ior and my God!

No. 145.
"Almost Persuaded."

P. P. B.

P. P. Bliss.

1. "Al-most per-suad-ed" now to be-lieve; "Al-most per-suad-ed"
2. "Al-most per-suad-ed," come, come to-day; "Al-most per-suad-ed,"
3. "Al-most per-suad-ed," har-vest is past! "Al-most per-suad-ed,"

Christ to re-ceive; Seems now some soul to say, "Go, Spir-it,
turn not a-way; Je-sus in-vites you here, An-gels are
doom comes at last! "Al-most" can-not a-vail; "Al-most" is

"Almost Persuaded."

go Thy way, Some more con-ven-ient day On Thee I'll call."
lin-g'ring near, Prayers rise from heart so dear, O wan-d'rer, come.
but to fail! Sad, sad, that bit-ter wail—"Al-most—but lost!"

No. 146 Why Not Come to Him Now?

F. A. S.

COPYRIGHT, 1908, BY E. O. EXCELL.
WORDS AND MUSIC.

Frank A. Simpson.

1. Sin-ner, why have you been straying? Why from the fold are you stay-ing?
2. Come, for the Sav-ior is call-ing; Come, e'er the night shades are fall-ing;
3. Come, for the moments are fly-ing; Come, sin's temptations de-fy-ing,
4. Friends whom you love are now sleeping, Oth-ers are pray-ing and weep-ing,

Loved ones for you have been pray-ing,
Life with-out Him is ap-pall-ing, Will you not come to Him now?..
While souls a-bout you are dy-ing,
An-gels their vig-ils are keep-ing, Will you not come to the Sav-ior now?

CHORUS.

Why not now? Why not now? Will you not come to Him now?
Why not now, O why not now? Why not now, O why not now?

No. 147. Let the Lower Lights Be Burning.

COPYRIGHT, 1905, BY THE JOHN CHURCH CO.
USED BY PERMISSION.

P. P. B.   P. P. Bliss.

1. Bright-ly beams our Fa-ther's mer-cy From His light-house ev-er more,
2. Dark the night of sin has set-tled, Loud the an-gry bil-lows roar;
3. Trim your fee-ble lamp, my brother: Some poor sail-or tem-pest tossed,

But to us He gives the keep-ing Of the lights a-long the shore.
Ea-ger eyes are watch-ing, long-ing, For the lights a-long the shore.
Try-ing now to make the har-bor, In the dark-ness may be lost.

D. S.—*Some poor fainting, struggling sea-man You may res-cue, you may save.*

CHORUS.

Let the low-er lights be burn-ing! Send a gleam a-cross the wave!

No. 148. God's Peace.

Anon.   H. G. B. Hunt.

1. We bless Thee for Thy peace, O God! Deep as the sound-less sea,
2. We ask not, Fa-ther, for re-pose Which comes from out-ward rest,
3. That peace which suf-fers and is strong, Trusts where it can-not see,
4. O Fa-ther, give our hearts this peace, What-e'er may out-ward be,

God's Peace.

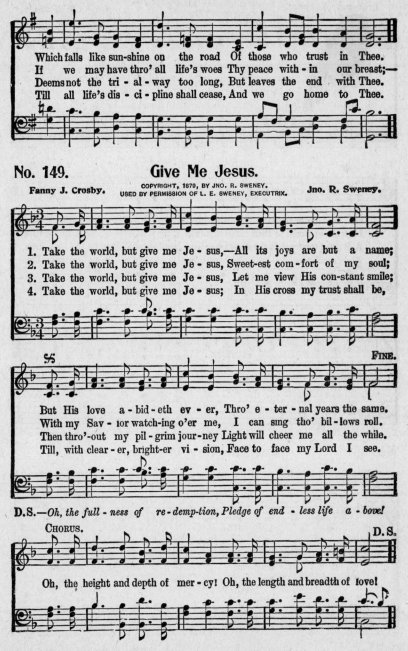

Which falls like sun-shine on   the road   Of those who trust   in   Thee.
If   we   may have thro' all   life's woes Thy peace with - in   our breast;—
Deems not the tri - al - way   too long, But leaves the   end   with Thee.
Till   all   life's dis - ci - pline shall cease, And we   go   home   to Thee.

No. 149.   Give Me Jesus.

Fanny J. Crosby.

Jno. R. Sweney.

1. Take the world, but give me Je - sus,—All its joys are but a name;
2. Take the world, but give me Je - sus, Sweet-est com - fort of my soul;
3. Take the world, but give me Je - sus, Let me view His con-stant smile;
4. Take the world, but give me Je - sus; In His cross my trust shall be,

FINE.

But His love a - bid - eth ev - er, Thro' e - ter - nal years the same.
With my Sav - ior watch-ing o'er me, I can sing tho' bil - lows roll.
Then thro'-out my pil - grim jour-ney Light will cheer me all the while.
Till, with clear - er, bright-er vi - sion, Face to face my Lord I see.

D.S.—*Oh, the full - ness of re - demp-tion, Pledge of end - less life a - bove!*

CHORUS.

D.S.

Oh, the height and depth of mer - cy! Oh, the length and breadth of love!

Faith of Our Fathers!

Frederick W. Faber.   H. F. Hemy, adpt.

1. Faith of our fa - thers! liv - ing still   In spite of dun-geon, fire and sword:
2. Our fathers, chained in pris-ons dark,   Were still in heart and conscience free;
3. Faith of our fa - thers, God's great pow'r Shall soon all nations win   for thee;
4. Faith of our fa - thers, we   will love Both friend and foe in all   our strife,

O   how our hearts beat high with joy, Whene'er we hear that glorious word:
How sweet would be their children's fate If they, like them, could die for thee!
And thro' the truth that comes from God, Mankind shall then be tru - ly free.
And preach thee, too, as love knows how, By kind-ly words and virtuous life.

Faith of our fa - thers! ho - ly faith! We will be true   to thee   till death.

No. 151.   **Now the Day is Over.**

Sabine Baring-Gould.   Joseph Barnby.

1. Now the day is   o - ver,   Night is draw - ing   nigh,
2. Je - sus, give the wear - y   Calm and sweet re - pose;
3. Grant to lit - tle chil - dren   Vi - sions bright of   Thee;
4. When the morn - ing wak - ens,   Then may I   a - rise

Now the Day is Over.

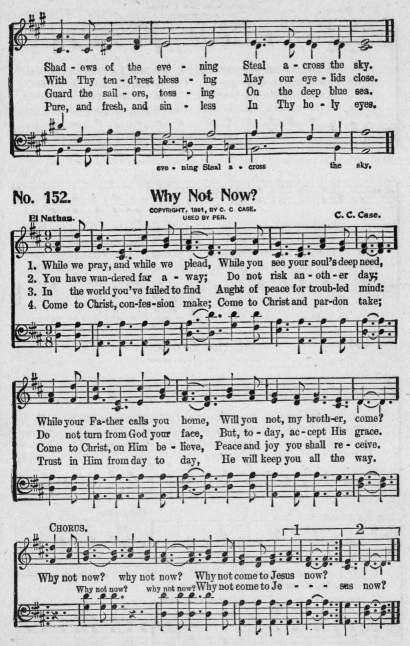

Shad - ows of the eve - ning Steal a - cross the sky.
With Thy ten - d'rest bless - ing May our eye - lids close.
Guard the sail - ors, toss - ing On the deep blue sea.
Pure, and fresh, and sin - less In Thy ho - ly eyes.

eve - ning Steal a - cross the sky.

No. 152.

Why Not Now?

COPYRIGHT, 1891, BY C. C. CASE.
USED BY PER.

El Nathan.

C. C. Case.

1. While we pray, and while we plead, While you see your soul's deep need,
2. You have wan-dered far a - way; Do not risk an - oth - er day;
3. In the world you've failed to find Aught of peace for troub-led mind:
4. Come to Christ, con-fes-sion make; Come to Christ and par-don take;

While your Fa-ther calls you home, Will you not, my broth-er, come?
Do not turn from God your face, But, to - day, ac-cept His grace.
Come to Christ, on Him be - lieve, Peace and joy you shall re - ceive.
Trust in Him from day to day, He will keep you all the way.

CHORUS.

1   2

Why not now? why not now? Why not come to Jesus now?
Why not now? why not now? Why not come to Je - - - sus now?

No. 153.   Where He Leads Me.

E. W. Blandly.

J. S. Norris.

1. I can hear my Sav - ior call - ing, I can hear my Sav - ior call - ing,
2. I'll go with Him thro' the gar-den, I'll go with Him thro' the gar-den,
3. I'll go with Him thro' the judgment, I'll go with Him thro' the judgment,
4. He will give me grace and glo - ry, He will give me grace and glo - ry,

D.C.—*Where He leads me I will fol - low, Where He leads me I will fol-low,*

D. C.

I can hear my Sav - ior call-ing, "Take thy cross and follow, fol-low Me."
I'll go with Him thro' the gar-den, I'll go with Him, with Him all the way.
I'll go with Him thro' the judgment, I'll go with Him, with Him all the way.
He will give me grace and glo - ry, And go with me, with me all the way.

Where He leads me I will fol - low, I'll go with Him, with Him all the way.

No. 154.   At the Cross.

Isaac Watts.

R. E. Hudson.

1. A - las, and did my Savior bleed? And did my Sov'reign die? Would He de-
2. Was it for crimes that I have done, He groaned upon the tree? A - maz-ing
3. Well might the sun in darkness hide, And shut his glo-ries in, When Christ, the
4. But drops of grief can ne'er re-pay The debt of love I owe: Here, Lord, I

CHORUS.

vote that sacred head For such a worm as I?
pit - y! grace unknown! And love beyond degree! At the cross, at the cross where I
mighty Maker, died For man, the creature's sin.
give my-self a-way, 'Tis all that I can do!

At the Cross.

first saw the light, And the burden of my heart rolled away, (rolled away,) It was

there by faith I received my sight, And now I am hap-py all the day!

No. 155.   I Love Him.

London Hymn Book.   USED BY PERMISSION.   S. C. Foster.

1. Gone from my heart the world and all its charm; Gone are my sins and
2. Once I was lost up - on the plains of sin; Once was a slave to
3. Once I was bound, but now I am set free; Once I was blind, but

all that would a - larm; Gone ev - er-more, and by His grace I know The
doubts and fears within; Once was a-fraid to trust a lov - ing God, But
now the light I see; Once I was dead, but now in Christ I live, To

D. S.—*Be-cause He first loved me, And*
FINE.   D. S.

precious blood of Je - sus cleanses white as snow.
now my guilt is washed away in Je-sus' blood. I love Him, I love Him,
tell the world the peace that He a - lone can give.

purcnased my sal - va - tion on Calv'ry's tree.

No. 156. Safely Through Another Week.

John Newton.   Arr. by Lowell Mason.

1. Safe - ly thro' an - oth - er week, God has bro't us on our way; Let us
2. While we pray for pard'ning grace, Thro' the dear Redeemer's name, Show Thy
3. Here we come Thy name to praise; Let us feel Thy presence near; May Thy
4. May the gos-pel's joy - ful sound Con-quer sin-ners, com-fort saints; Make the

now a bless - ing seek, Wait - ing in His courts to - day. Day of
rec - on - cil - ed face, Take a - way our sin and shame; From our
glo - ry meet our eyes, While we in Thy house ap - pear; Here af -
fruits of grace a - bound, Bring re - lief to all com-plaints; Thus may

all the week the best, Emblem of e - ter - nal rest; of e - ter - nal rest.
world-ly cares set free, May we rest this day in Thee; rest this day in Thee.
ford us, Lord, a taste Of our ev - er - last-ing feast, ev - er - last-ing feast.
all our Sabbaths prove, Till we join the church a-bove; join the church a - bove.

No. 157. Savior, More Than Life.

Fanny J. Crosby.

W. H. Doane.

1. Sav - ior, more than life to me, I am clinging, clinging close to Thee;
2. Thro' this changing world be - low, Lead me gen-tly, gen-tly as I go;
3. Let me love Thee more and more, Till this fleeting, fleet-ing life is o'er;

Savior, More Than Life.

Let Thy pre-cious blood ap-plied, Keep me ev-er, ev-er near Thy side.
Trusting Thee, I can-not stray, I can nev-er, nev-er lose my way.
Till my soul is lost in love, In a bright-er, brighter world a-bove.

D. S.—May Thy ten-der love to me Bind me clos-er, clos-er, Lord, to Thee.

REFRAIN.

D. S.

Ev-'ry day, ev-'ry hour, Let me feel Thy cleansing pow'r;
Ev-'ry day and hour, ev-'ry day and hour,

No. 158.   Pass Me Not.

Fanny J. Crosby.   W. H. DOANE, OWNER OF COPYRIGHT.   USED BY PER.   W. H. Doane.

1. Pass me not, O gen-tle Sav-ior, Hear my hum-ble cry; While on oth-ers
2. Let me at a throne of mer-cy Find a sweet re-lief; Kneel-ing there in
3. Trust-ing on-ly in Thy mer-it, Would I seek Thy face; Heal my wounded,
4. Thou the Spring of all my com-fort, More than life to me, Whom have I on

D. S.—While on oth-ers

FINE. CHORUS.

D. S.

Thou art call-ing, Do not pass me by.
deep con-tri-tion, Help my un-be-lief. Sav-ior, Sav-ior, Hear my humble cry;
bro-ken spir-it, Save me by Thy grace.
earth beside Thee? Whom in Heav'n but Thee?

Thou art call-ing, Do not pass me by.

No. 159. Holy Bible, Book Divine.

John Burton. COPYRIGHT 1900, BY E. O. EXCELL. E. O. Excell.

Slow, with dignity.

1. Ho - ly Bi - ble, Book di - vine, Pre-cious treas-ure, thou art mine:
2. Mine to chide me when I rove; Mine to show a Sav-ior's love;
3. Mine to com-fort in dis-tress, Suf-f'ring in this wil - der - ness;
4. Mine to tell of joys to come, And the reb - el sin-ner's doom:

Mine to tell me whence I came; Mine to tell me what I am;
Mine thou art to guide and guard; Mine to pun - ish or re - ward;
Mine to show, by liv - ing faith, Man can tri - umph o - ver death;
O thou ho - ly Book di - vine, Pre-cious treas-ure, thou art mine.

rit.

CHORUS.

Ho - ly Bi - ble, Book di - vine, Pre-cious treas - ure, thou art mine;

O thou ho - ly Book di - vine, Pre-cious treas - ure, thou art mine!

CHILDREN'S SONGS

No. 160.

I'll Be a Sunbeam.

To my grandson, Edwin O. Excell, Jr.

Nellie Talbot.

E. O. Excell.

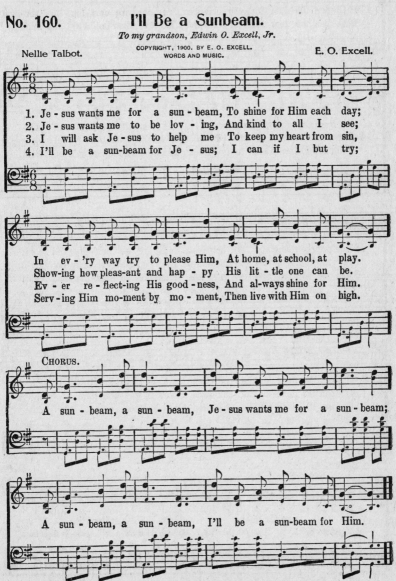

1. Je-sus wants me for a sun-beam, To shine for Him each day;
2. Je-sus wants me to be lov-ing, And kind to all I see;
3. I will ask Je-sus to help me To keep my heart from sin,
4. I'll be a sun-beam for Je-sus; I can if I but try;

In ev-'ry way try to please Him, At home, at school, at play.
Show-ing how pleas-ant and hap-py His lit-tle one can be.
Ev-er re-flect-ing His good-ness, And al-ways shine for Him.
Serv-ing Him mo-ment by mo-ment, Then live with Him on high.

CHORUS.

A sun-beam, a sun-beam, Je-sus wants me for a sun-beam;

A sun-beam, a sun-beam, I'll be a sun-beam for Him.

No. 161. Open the Door for the Children.

Mary B. Kidder. COPYRIGHT, 1885, BY E. O. EXCELL. E. O. Excell.

1. O - pen the door for the chil - dren, Ten - der - ly gath - er them in,—
2. O - pen the door for the chil - dren, See, they are com - ing in throngs!
3. O - pen the door for the chil - dren, Take the dear lambs by the hand;

In from the high-ways and hedg - es, In from the plac - es of sin;
Bid them sit down to the ban - quet, Teach them your beau - ti - ful songs;
Point them to truth and to good-ness, Lead them to Ca-naan's fair land.

Some are so young and so help-less, Some are so hun-gry and cold;
Pray for the Fa - ther to bless them, Pray you that grace may be giv'n;
Some are so young and so help-less, Some are so hun-gry and cold;

D. S.—O - pen the door for the chil - dren, Gath - er them in - to the fold.
O - pen the door for the chil - dren, Theirs is the king-dom of heav'n.
O - pen the door for the chil - dren, Gath - er them in - to the fold.

CHORUS.

O - pen the door, . . . Gath - er them in, ...
O - pen the door, o - pen the door, Gath - er them in, gath - er them in,

No. 162.　Jesus Was a Child Like Me.

(Primary.)

Fanny J. Crosby.　　　　W. H. Doane.

1. Once Je-sus was　a child like me, But O, so kind and true;
2. He played up-on　the vil-lage street, In such a pleas-ant way;
3. I　want to be His lit-tle child, And more like Him to grow;
4. And now to Je-sus I　will pray, To par-don me from sin;

His ev-er watch-ful eye can see The ver-y things I　do.
And ran with glad and will-ing feet, His par-ents to　o-bey.
And ev-er truth-ful, good and mild, Be-cause He loves me　so.
And if I serve Him ev-'ry day, His bless-ing I　shall win.

Chorus.

Yes, Je-sus was　a child like me, But O, so pure and true;

My bless-ed Sav-ior He will be, If I　but love Him too.

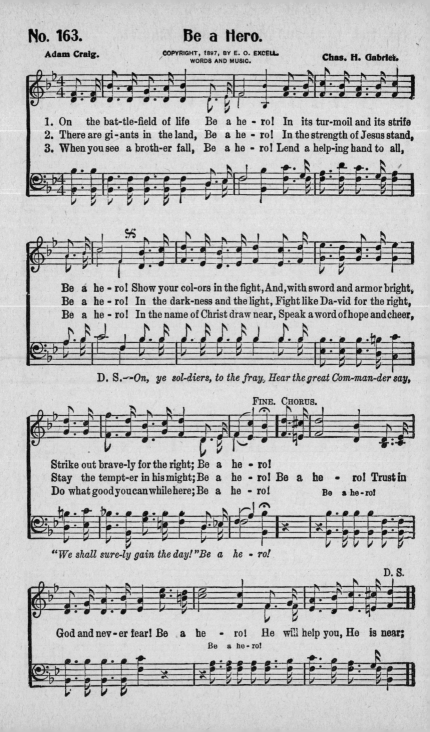

No. 163. Be a Hero.

Adam Craig.

Chas. H. Gabriel.

1. On the bat-tle-field of life   Be a he - ro! In its tur-moil and its strife
2. There are gi-ants in the land, Be a he - ro! In the strength of Jesus stand,
3. When you see a broth-er fall, Be a he - ro! Lend a help-ing hand to all,

Be a he - ro! Show your col-ors in the fight, And, with sword and armor bright,
Be a he - ro! In the dark-ness and the light, Fight like Da-vid for the right,
Be a he - ro! In the name of Christ draw near, Speak a word of hope and cheer,

D. S.—On, ye sol-diers, to the fray, Hear the great Com-man-der say,

FINE. CHORUS.

Strike out brave-ly for the right; Be a he - ro!
Stay the tempt-er in his might; Be a he - ro! Be a he - ro! Trust in
Do what good you can while here; Be a he - ro!

Be a he - ro!

"We shall sure-ly gain the day!" Be a he - ro!

D. S.

God and nev-er fear! Be a he - ro! He will help you, He is near;

Be a he - ro!

Little Sunbeams.

Eben E. Rexford.

Chas. H. Gabriel.

1. I think God gives the chil-dren, As thro' the land they go, The
2. The clouds may hide the sun-shine Of heav-en from our sight, And
3. Then let us live our mis-sion Of sun-beams day by day, And

most de-light-ful mis-sion That an-y one can know; He wants us to be
life have much of sor-row To mar the heart's delight; But if like faith-ful
scat-ter joy and brightness A-bout us all the way; Let's chase a-way life's

sun-beams Of love, and hope, and cheer, To bright-en up the shad-ows That
sun-beams, We chil-dren do our part, We'll bring a ray of brightness To
shad-ows With lov-ing tho't and deed, And be the sun-shine-ma-kers Of

CHORUS.

oft-en gath-er here.
ev-'ry shadowed heart. O we are lit-tle sun-beams, Sent down from God to
which the world has need.

man; In all life's sha-dy pla-ces We shine as best we can.

No. 165. Sunshine and Rain.

C. H. G.

Chas. H. Gabriel.

1. Had we on-ly sun-shine all the year a-round, With-out the bless-ing
2. Had we not a sor-row or a cross to bear, For Him who bore the
3. Can we prize the sun-shine and de-plore the rain, Re-pin-ing when the

of re-fresh-ing rain, Would we scat-ter seed up-on the fallow ground,
bur-den of our sin, Would we know the sweetness of His love and care,
days are dark and drear? Can we hope for pleasures, yet de-ny the pain,

CHORUS.

And hope to gath-er flow-ers, fruit and grain?
Or e-ven strive e-ter-nal joys to win? Sun-shine and rain, re-
Or share the joys of life with-out the tear?

freshing, reviving rain, Light of faith and love, Showers from above! Sunshine and

rain, to nour-ish the growing grain, Send us, Lord, the sunshine and the rain.

No. 166. Let the Sunshine In.

Ada Blenkhorn.

Chas. H. Gabriel.

1. Do you fear the foe will in the con-flict win? Is it dark with-
2. Does your faith grow faint-er in the cause you love? Are your prayers un-
3. Would you go re-joi-cing in the up-ward way, Know-ing naught of

out you—dark-er still with-in? Clear the dark-ened windows, o-pen
an-swered by your God a-bove? Clear the dark-ened windows, o-pen
dark-ness, dwell-ing in the day? Clear the dark-ened windows, o-pen

CHORUS.

wide the door, Let a lit-tle sun-shine in. Let a lit-tle sun-shine
the

in, ... Let a lit-tle sun-shine in; .... Clear the dark-ened
sun-shine in, the sun-shine in;

win-dows, o-pen wide the door, Let a lit-tle sun-shine in.

No. 167. Angry Words! Oh, Let Them Never.

H. R. P. USED BY PERMISSION OF DR. H. R. PALMER, OWNER OF COPYRIGHT. Dr. H. R. Palmer.

1. An - gry words! oh, let them nev - er From the tongue un-bri - dled slip;
2. Love is much too pure and ho - ly; Friendship is too sa - cred far,
3. An - gry words are light-ly spo - ken; Bit-t'rest tho'ts are rash-ly stirred—

May the heart's best im-pulse ev - er Check them, ere they soil the lip.
For a mo-ment's reckless fol - ly Thus to des - o - late and mar.
Bright-est links of life are bro - ken By a sin-gle an - gry word.

CHORUS.

"Love one an - oth - er," thus saith the Sav - ior, Chil-dren, o-
Love each oth - er, love each oth - er,

bey the Fa - ther's blest com - mand: bey His blest com - mand.
'Tis the Fa - ther's blest com - mand: 'Tis His blest com - mand.

Rose, Rose, Rose.

Charlotte G. Homer.

Chas. H. Gabriel.

1. What is sweeter, tell me, Than a pret-ty
2. If a rose could whisper, Could it, think you,
3. Je - sus, keep me ev - er Like un-to this

Waltz time.

rose? Fra-grant in its beau - ty, Loveliest flow'r that grows.
tell Of that bless-ed coun - try Where the an-gels dwell?
flow'r— Pure and sweet and mod-est, Ev - 'ry day and hour.

REFRAIN.

Rose, rose, rose, Pret - ti - est flow'r that grows, Em-blem of
Rose, rose, rose, Not till the whole world knows Of my dear

1

love that came from heaven, Thro' which a Savior, Christ, was giv-en;

2

Sav - ior King, Will I cease to sing, Sweet rose, rose, rose. . .

No. 169.

We'll Never Say Fail.

Lizzie DeArmond.
Unison.

W. A. Post.

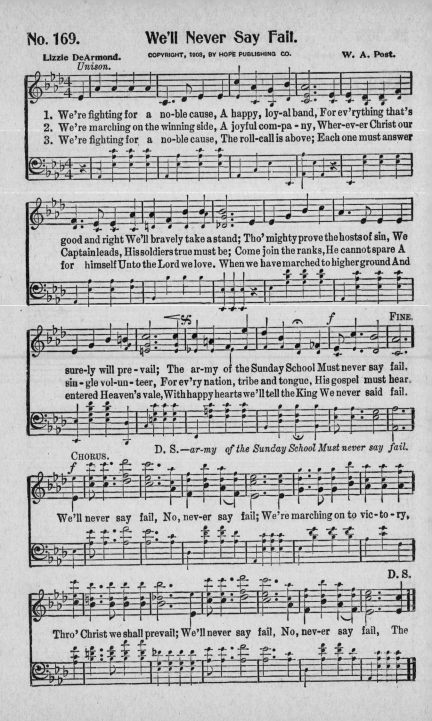

1. We're fighting for a no-ble cause, A happy, loy-al band, For ev'rything that's good and right We'll bravely take a stand; Tho' mighty prove the hosts of sin, We sure-ly will pre-vail; The ar-my of the Sunday School Must never say fail.

2. We're marching on the winning side, A joyful com-pa-ny, Wher-ev-er Christ our Captain leads, His soldiers true must be; Come join the ranks, He cannot spare A sin-gle vol-un-teer, For ev'ry nation, tribe and tongue, His gospel must hear.

3. We're fighting for a no-ble cause, The roll-call is above; Each one must answer for himself Unto the Lord we love. When we have marched to higher ground And entered Heaven's vale, With happy hearts we'll tell the King We never said fail.

D. S.—ar-my of the Sunday School Must never say fail.

CHORUS.

We'll never say fail, No, nev-er say fail; We're marching on to vic-to-ry,

D. S.

Thro' Christ we shall prevail; We'll never say fail, No, nev-er say fail, The

No. 170. The Birds' Nest.

Mrs. B. B. Selby, Arr.

COPYRIGHT, 1911, BY E. O. EXCELL.
WORDS AND MUSIC.

E. O. Excell.

1. ¹High in the treetop's leaf-y bough The bird-ies are build-ing a nest;
2. ²This is the lit-tle bird-ies' nest They built in the tree-top so high,
3. ³This is the mother bird who brings The wee ⁴lit-tle bird-ies their food;
4. ⁶These are the lit-tle birds we love, Who live in the tree-top so high,

'Twas God the Father taught them how To build, ev-'ry bird-ie his best;
And while they cud-dle down to rest The leaves sing their lull-a-by-by;
This is the ⁵fa-ther bird who sings And watches all day o'er his brood;
And He who rules the ⁸world a-bove Looks ⁹down on each one from the sky;

To build, ev-'ry bird-ie his best, To build ev-'ry bird-ie his best,
The leaves sing their lull-a-by-by, The leaves sing their lull-a-by-by,
And watch-es all day o'er his brood, And watch-es all day o'er his brood,
Looks ⁹down on each one from the sky, Looks ⁹down on each one from the sky,

'Twas God the Fa-ther taught them how To build, ev-'ry bird-ie his best.
And while they cud-dle down to rest The leaves sing their lull-a-by-by.
This is the ⁵fa-ther bird who sings And watches all day o'er his brood.
And He who rules the ⁸world a-bove Looks ⁹down on each one from the sky.

NOTE—To form bird's nest clasp hands, with little fingers raised in the palm of the hands to represent the baby birds. Let the thumbs represent the father and mother bird sitting on the forefingers which form the edge of the bird's nest.

MOTIONS—1, Point upward to treetop; 2, Hands clasped to form bird's nest; 3, Raise left hand thumb to represent the mother bird; 4, Raise little fingers representing the baby birds; 5, Raise right hand thumb representing the father bird; 6, Raise little fingers and thumbs representing the family of birds in the nest; 7, Point upward to treetop; 8, Look upward toward the sky; 9, Look down on the birds in the nest.

No. 171. Honor-Bright Cadets.

C. B. A.

Mrs. Carrie B. Adams.

1. { We're ca-dets that want to bat-tle for the right, you see; That is why we
   { For our watch-word we have chosen "Honor bright!" you see, [Omit.] . . . .

2. { We're de-ter-mined that we'll never know de-feat, you see; If we fight for
   { For our Lead-er nev-er taught us to re-treat, you see, [Omit.] . . . .

band ourselves together; And we'll keep it up in ev-'ry kind of weather.
right, we'll win the battle; No matter how the guns and sabers rattle.

For the right, then; Honor bright, then; We will march on our journey thro' the world;
We'll be strong, then, 'Gainst the wrong, then, And we'll work till the setting of the sun;

Col-ors fly-ing, Ev-er try-ing To be true, as our banner is un-furled.
Col-ors fly-ing, Ev-er try-ing To be faithful un-til the vict'ry's won.

CHORUS.

{ Then see us marching as to war; . . . With purpose steady, Our hearts are
{ Our gal-lant Lead-er goes be- [Omit.] . . . .

Honor-Bright Cadets.

read-y; ... fore:... Then see us march! We are "Honor-Bright Cadets!"

No. 172.   ## Dear Little Stranger.

C. H. G.   COPYRIGHT, 1900, BY E. O. EXCELL.   Chas. H. Gabriel.
WORDS AND MUSIC.

1. Low in a man-ger—dear lit-tle Stran-ger, Je-sus, the won-der-ful
2. An-gels de-scend-ing, o-ver Him bend-ing, Chant-ed a ten-der and
3. Dear lit-tle Stran-ger, born in a man-ger, Mak-er and Monarch, and

Savior, was born; There was none to receive Him, none to believe Him, None but the
si-lent refrain; Then a won-der-ful sto-ry told of His glo-ry, Un-to the
Sav-ior of all; I will love Thee for-ev-er! grieve Thee? no, never! Thou didst for

an-gels were watching that morn. ⎱ Dear lit-tle Stranger, slept in a man-ger,
shepherds on Bethlehem's plain. ⎰ But with the poor He slumbered se-cure, The
me make Thy bed in a stall.

CHORUS.

No down-y pil-low un-der His head; dear lit-tle Babe in His bed.

No. 173. The Children's Hosanna.

Neal A. McAuley.

J. S. Fearis.

1. I dreamed one night, not long a-go, Of man-sions in the skies, Where
2. And, as I mused, I heard a voice, In sweet-er tones than all, Di-
3. And when from slumber I a-rose, To serve my Lord and King, I

those who love the Lord ob-tain A rich and glo-rious prize; I saw a-mong the
rect-ing Christian workers here, In words I now re-call: "Forbid them not," He
felt that I the lit-tle lambs To Christ in love might bring; And then I cried for

hap-py throng The children bright and fair; I heard their voi-ces clear and sweet
gen-tly said, "The children bring to Me; Their por-tion in the World of Light
dai-ly grace Their precious souls to cheer, Till they could sing, like yonder choir,

REFRAIN. *Faster.*

With mu-sic fill the air."
Redeemed shall ev-er be." Ho-san-na! Ho-san-na! Our songs of love we bring!
Ho-san-na! bright and clear.

we bring!

Ho-san-na! Ho-san-na! To Christ, the children's King; Ho-san-na! Ho-san-na!

The Children's Hosanna.

Our songs of love we bring, Ho-san-na! Ho-san-na! to Christ, the children's King.
we bring.

No 174.

Bring Them In.

Alexcenah Thomas.   COPYRIGHT, 1885, BY W. A. OGDEN. USED BY PERMISSION.   **W. A. Ogden.**

1. Hark! 'tis the Shepherd's voice I hear, Out in the des-ert dark and drear,
2. Who'll go and help this Shepherd kind, Help Him the wand'ring ones to find?
3. Out in the des-ert hear their cry, Out on the mountains wild and high;

Call-ing the sheep who've gone astray Far from the Shepherd's fold a-way.
Who'll bring the lost ones to the fold, Where they'll be sheltered from the cold?
Hark! 'tis the Mas-ter speaks to thee, "Go find my sheep wher-e'er they be."

CHORUS.

Bring them in, bring them in, Bring them in from the fields of sin;

Bring them in, bring them in, Bring the wand'ring ones to Je-sus.

No. 175.

Under the Snow.

Mary Gilbert-Wray.

Chas. H. Gabriel.

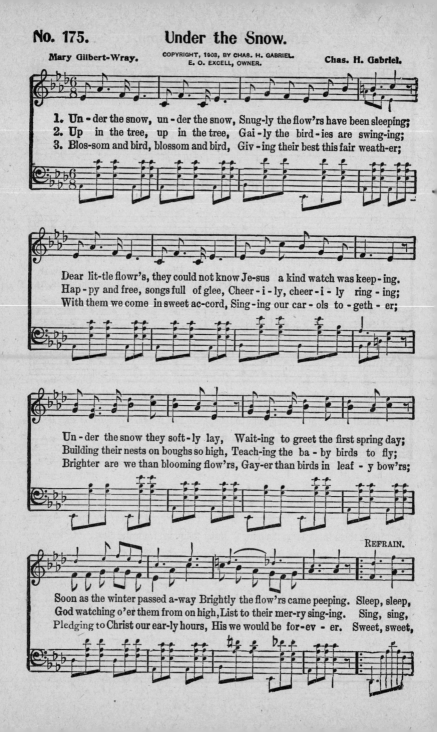

1. Un - der the snow, un - der the snow, Snug-ly the flow'rs have been sleeping;
2. Up in the tree, up in the tree, Gai - ly the bird-ies are swing-ing;
3. Blos-som and bird, blossom and bird, Giv-ing their best this fair weath-er;

Dear lit-tle flowr's, they could not know Je-sus a kind watch was keep-ing.
Hap-py and free, songs full of glee, Cheer - i - ly, cheer - i - ly ring - ing;
With them we come in sweet ac-cord, Sing-ing our car - ols to-geth - er;

Un - der the snow they soft-ly lay, Wait-ing to greet the first spring day;
Building their nests on boughs so high, Teach-ing the ba - by birds to fly;
Brighter are we than blooming flow'rs, Gay-er than birds in leaf - y bow'rs;

REFRAIN.

Soon as the winter passed a-way Brightly the flow'rs came peeping. Sleep, sleep,
God watching o'er them from on high, List to their mer-ry sing-ing. Sing, sing,
Pledging to Christ our ear-ly hours, His we would be for-ev - er. Sweet, sweet,

Under the Snow.

sleep, sleep, 'Neath a blanket of drift-ed snow; Not a sorrow you know.
sing, sing, Swing your cradle up in the tree; Car - ol hap-py and free.
sweet, sweet, Bird and blossom and busy bee; God will watch over thee.

No. 176.   Jesus Bids Us Shine.

COPYRIGHT, 1884 BY E O. EXCELL.

E. O. Excell.

1. Je - sus bids us shine, With a clear, pure light, Like a lit - tle
2. Je - sus bids us shine, First of all for Him; Well He sees and
3. Je - sus bids us shine, Then, for all a - round Man - y kinds of
4. Je - sus bids us shine, As we work for Him, Bring-ing those that

can - dle Burn - ing in the night; In this world of dark - ness
knows it If our light is dim; He looks down from heav - en,
dark - ness In this world a - bound,—Sin and want and sor - row;
wan - der From the paths of sin; He will ev - er help us,

We must shine, You in your small cor - ner, And I in mine.
Sees us shine, You in your small cor - ner, And I in mine.
We must shine, You in your small cor - ner, And I in mine.
If we shine, You in your small cor - ner, And I in mine.

No. 177.   Onward, Little Soldiers!

James Rowe.

COPYRIGHT, 1902, BY CHAS. H. GABRIEL.
E O. EXCELL, OWNER.

Martin A. Elliott

1. On-ward, lit-tle sol-diers, Brave-ly on-ward go; Learn to trust in
2. On-ward, lit-tle sol-diers, In the gos-pel light; Keep your ban-ner
3. On-ward, lit-tle sol-diers, On-ward ev-'ry day, Full of love for

Je - sus, Learn to face the foe. Je - sus is your Lead-er,
wav-ing, And your ar-mor bright. Fol-low Je - sus close-ly,
Je - sus, Ea-ger for the fray. Ev-'ry hour that pass-es,

And your soul will shield; On-ward, lit - tle sol-diers, To the bat-tle-field.
And from fear be free; Let your weapons al-ways Love and kind-ness be.
E - ven you may win Vic - to-ries for Je - sus, O-ver doubt and sin.

No. 178.   Jesus Loves Me.

Wm. B. Bradbury.

1. Je - sus loves me! this I know, For the Bi - ble tells me so;
2. Je - sus loves me! He who died, Heav-en's gate to o - pen wide;
3. Je - sus loves me! loves me still, Tho' I'm ver - y weak and ill;
4. Je - sus loves me! He will stay Close be - side me all the way;

Jesus Loves Me.

Lit - tle ones to Him be - long, They are weak but He is strong.
He will wash a - way my sin, Let His lit - tle child come in.
From His shin-ing throne on high, Comes to watch me where I lie.
If I love Him when I die, He will take me home on high.

CHORUS.

Yes, Jesus loves me, Yes, Jesus loves me, Yes, Jesus loves me, The Bible tells me so.

No. 179. Growing Up For Jesus.

Miriam E. Arnold. COPYRIGHT, 1906, BY CHAS. H. GABRIEL. Chas. H. Gabriel.
E. O. EXCELL, OWNER.

1. Grow-ing up for Je - sus, In His vine-yard fair, Ev-er watched and
2. Keep us free, dear Je - sus, From sin's hurt-ful weeds; Prune us, Lord, and
3. Gen - tle, kind, and lov - ing, Sav-ior, may we be; Thou a - lone canst

CHORUS.

tend - ed By His lov - ing care.
train us, Care for all our needs! Ten - der lit - tle branch-es,
help us Bear "much fruit" for Thee.

Grow-ing up for Thee; Fruit-ful vines, dear Master, We would like to be.

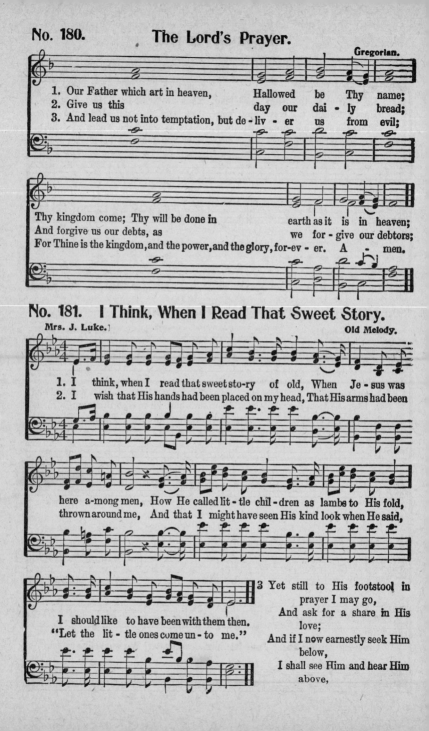

No. 180. The Lord's Prayer.
No. 181. I Think, When I Read That Sweet Story.

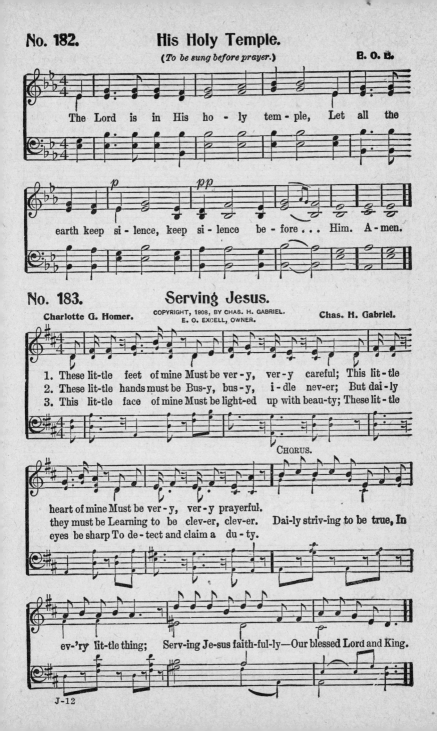

No. 182.

His Holy Temple.

(To be sung before prayer.)

B. O. E.

The Lord is in His ho-ly tem-ple, Let all the earth keep si-lence, keep si-lence be-fore ... Him. A-men.

No. 183.

Serving Jesus.

Charlotte G. Homer.

COPYRIGHT, 1908, BY CHAS. H. GABRIEL.
E. O. EXCELL, OWNER.

Chas. H. Gabriel.

1. These lit-tle feet of mine Must be ver-y, ver-y careful; This lit-tle
2. These lit-tle hands must be Bus-y, bus-y, i-dle nev-er; But dai-ly
3. This lit-tle face of mine Must be light-ed up with beau-ty; These lit-tle

CHORUS.

heart of mine Must be ver-y, ver-y prayerful.
they must be Learning to be clev-er, clev-er.
eyes be sharp To de-tect and claim a du-ty.

Dai-ly striv-ing to be true, In

ev-'ry lit-tle thing; Serv-ing Je-sus faith-ful-ly—Our blessed Lord and King.

J-12

No. 184. Jesus Loves Even Me.

COPYRIGHT, 1902, BY THE JOHN CHURCH CO.
USED BY PERMISSION.

P. P. B.   P. P. Bliss.

1. I am so glad that our Fa-ther in Heav'n Tells of His love in the Book He has giv'n; Won-der-ful things in the Bi-ble I see;

2. Tho' I for-get Him and wan-der a-way, Still He doth love me wher-ev-er I stray; Back to His dear lov-ing arms would I flee,

3. Oh, if there's on-ly one song I can sing, When in His beau-ty I see the Great King, This shall my song in e-ter-ni-ty be:

CHORUS.

This is the dear-est—that Je-sus loves me.
When I re-mem-ber that Je-sus loves me.
"Oh, what a won-der that Je-sus loves me!"

I am so glad that Je-sus loves me, Je-sus loves me, Je-sus loves me; e-ven me.

No. 185. Jesus Loves Me.

1 Jesus loves me, and I know I love Him,
Love brought Him down my poor soul to redeem:
Yes, it was love made Him die on the tree,
Oh, I am certain that Jesus loves me.

Cho.—I am so glad, etc.

2 If one should ask of me, how could I tell!
Glory to Jesus, I know very well:
God's Holy Spirit with mine doth agree,
Constantly witnessing—Jesus loves me.

Cho.—I am so glad, etc.

3 In this assurance I find sweetest rest,
Trusting in Jesus, I know I am blest;
Satan, dismayed, from my soul now doth flee,
When I just tell Him that Jesus loves me.—Cho.

SPECIAL SELECTIONS

No. 186.

Happy Song-Land.

COPYRIGHT, 1903, BY E. O. EXCELL.

C. A. H.

C. A. Havens.

Melody prominent.

1. Song-land fair, O - ver there, Free from sorrow, free from care; Angels bright,
2. Toils are o'er, Near the shore, Near the blessed Ev - er-more; Hand in hand,

Robed in white, Dwell in peace and pure de-light. By and by, Shadows nigh,
Near the strand, Near the shin-ing Summer Land; Where we go, Fountains flow

D. S.—*By and by, Shadows nigh,*

f

Resting comes in home on high; We shall join in prais-es there, In that happy
In the noon-tide's sunny glow; Joyful ransomed souls are there, In that happy

Rest-ing comes in home on high; We shall join in praises there, In that happy

REFRAIN.

FINE. *f*

D. S.

rit.

Song-land fair. Ho - ly, hap-py Song-land fair, Radiant mansions 'wait us there;
Song-land fair.

Song-land fair.

No. 187. He Loves Even Me.

S. L.

Scott Lawrence.

1. When I think of my Sav-ior's great love, In com-ing from Heav-en a-
2. When I think of the thorns on His brow, Seems as if I can see Je-sus
3. When I think how He saves me from sin, Though oft-en un-grate-ful I've

bove, To die on the tree For a sin-ner like me, I am sure that He
now, As He suf-fered for me, That my soul might be free: I am sure that He
been, My vow I re-new, "To be faith-ful and true;" I am sure that He

Chorus.

loves e-ven me. I am sure that He loves e-ven me, ...

I am sure that He loves e-ven me; . . . . And His love is so

sweet, Makes my joy so complete When I think how He loves e-ven me. . . . .

He Knows It All.

Mrs. Ophelia Adams.

C. M. Davis.

1. I love to think my Fa-ther knows Why I have missed the path I chose,
2. I love to think my Fa-ther knows The thorns I pluck with ev-'ry rose,
3. I love to think my Fa-ther knows The strength or weakness of my foes,

And that I soon shall clear-ly see The way He led was best for me.
The dai-ly griefs I seek to hide From the dear souls I walk be-side.
And that I need but stand and see Each con-flict end in vic-to-ry.

REFRAIN.

He knows it all, . . . He knows it all, . . . My Fa-ther
He knows it all, He knows it all,

knows, . . He knows it all; . . . Thy bit-ter tears . . . how
My Fa-ther knows He knows it all; Thy bit-ter tears

fast they fall!— He knows, My Fa-ther knows it all.
how fast they fall!—

No. 189.   I Died Broken-Hearted.

Rev. A. H. Ackley.   COPYRIGHT, 1914, BY E. O. EXCELL.   WORDS AND MUSIC.   B. D. Ackley.
INTERNATIONAL COPYRIGHT.

DUET.

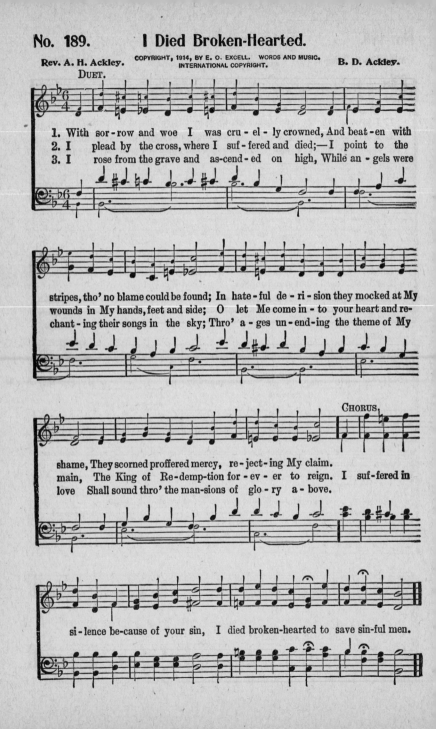

1. With sor-row and woe I was cru-el-ly crowned, And beat-en with
2. I plead by the cross, where I suf-fered and died;—I point to the
3. I rose from the grave and as-cend-ed on high, While an-gels were

stripes, tho' no blame could be found; In hate-ful de-ri-sion they mocked at My
wounds in My hands, feet and side; O let Me come in-to your heart and re-
chant-ing their songs in the sky; Thro' a-ges un-end-ing the theme of My

CHORUS.

shame, They scorned proffered mercy, re-ject-ing My claim.
main, The King of Re-demp-tion for-ev-er to reign. I suf-fered in
love Shall sound thro' the man-sions of glo-ry a-bove.

si-lence be-cause of your sin, I died broken-hearted to save sin-ful men.

No. 190. Better Than I Know.

Ina Duley Ogdon.

B. D. Ackley.

1. Christ found me lost in sor-row's night, Up-on my soul a crim-son blight;
2. He drew me to His lov-ing heart, And bade me nev-er-more de-part;
3. When I, in weak-ness, al-most fail, Still does His love for me pre-vail,

My stain of sin He made as snow,—He loves me bet-ter than I know.
No love like His, a-bove, be-low,—He loves me bet-ter than I know.
Still does He grace and mer-cy show; He loves me bet-ter than I know.

CHORUS.

He loves me bet-ter than I know; Wher-e'er I stray His love will go—

There is no oth-er loves me so, He loves me bet-ter than I know.

No. 191.

Jesus Will!

Ina Duley Ogdon.

B. D. Ackley.

DUET.

1. Who will o - pen mer-cy's door? Je-sus will! Je-sus will!
2. Who can take a - way my sin? Je-sus will! Je-sus will!
3. Who can conquer doubts and fears? Je-sus will! Je-sus will!
4. Who will be my dear-est Friend? Je-sus will! Je-sus will!

As   for par - don I im - plore? Je-sus, bless-ed Je - sus will!
Make me pure, with-out, with - in? Je-sus, bless-ed Je - sus will!
Share my joys and dry my tears? Je-sus, bless-ed Je - sus will!
Love and keep me to the end? Je-sus, bless-ed Je - sus will!

CHORUS.

Je - sus will,   Je - sus will! Yes, your lov-ing Sav-ior will;

sure - ly will;

He will each and ev - 'ry need ful-fill, Je-sus, bless-ed Je-sus will!

No. 192. I Am Happy in Him.

E. O. E.

E. O. Excell.

1. My soul is so hap-py in Je - sus, For He is so precious to me;
2. He sought me so long ere I knew Him, When wand'ring afar from the fold;
3. His love and His mer-cy surround me, His grace like a riv-er doth flow;
4. They say I shall some day be like Him, My cross and my burden lay down;

His voice it is music to hear it, His face it is heaven to see.
Safe home in His arms He hath bro't me, To where there are pleasures untold.
His Spir - it, to guide and to comfort, Is with me wher-ev-er I go.
Till then I will ev-er be faith-ful, In gath - er-ing gems for His crown.

CHORUS.

I am hap-py in Him, . . I am hap-py in Him; . .
I . . . . am hap-py in Him, I . . . . am hap-py in Him;

My soul with de-light He fills day and night, For I am hap-py in Him.

No. 193. Because His Name is Jesus.

Arr. by E. O. E.

E. O. Excell.

1. In vain I've tried a thousand ways My fears to quell, my hopes to raise,
2. My soul is night, my heart is steel, I can-not see, I can-not feel;
3. He died for me, He lives, He pleads, There's love in all His words and deeds;
4. Tho' some will scorn, and some will blame, I'll go with all my guilt and shame,

But what I need thro' all my days Is Je - sus, is Je - sus.
For light, for life, I must ap - peal To Je - sus, to Je - sus.
There's all a guilt - y sin - ner needs In Je - sus, in Je - sus.
I'll go to Him be - cause His name Is Je - sus, is Je - sus.

No. 194.   Somebody Knows.

Alfred H. Ackley.

B. D. Ackley.

Legato.

1. Failing in strength when opprest by my foes, Somebody knows, Somebody knows;
2. Why should I fear when the care-billows roll? Somebody knows, Somebody knows;
3. Wounded and helpless and sick with distress, Somebody knows, Somebody knows;

Wait - ing for some one to banish my woes, Somebody knows—'t is Je - sus.
When the deep shadows sweep over my soul, Somebody knows—'t is Je - sus.
Long - ing for home and a mother's ca-ress, Somebody knows—'t is Je - sus.

CHORUS.

Somebody knows, Somebody knows When I am tempted and tried by my foes;

rit.

He is the One who will keep me—Some-bod-y knows—'t is Je - sus.

No. 195. My Father Knows.

S. M. I. Henry.

E. O. Excell.

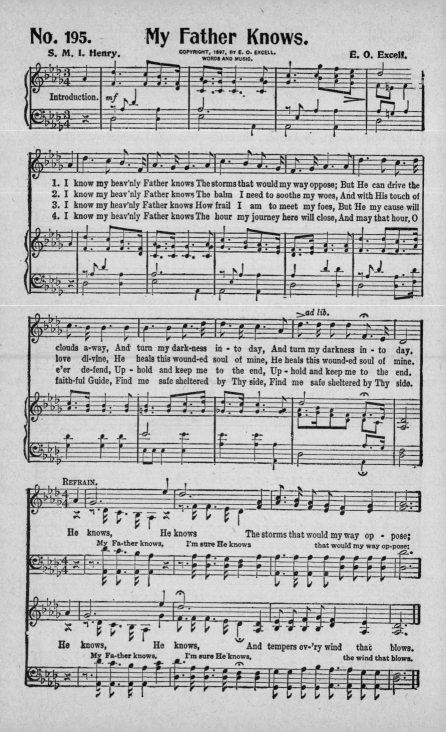

Introduction. *mf*

1. I know my heav'nly Father knows The storms that would my way oppose; But He can drive the
2. I know my heav'nly Father knows The balm I need to soothe my woes, And with His touch of
3. I know my heav'nly Father knows How frail I am to meet my foes, But He my cause will
4. I know my heav'nly Father knows The hour my journey here will close, And may that hour, O

ad lib.

clouds a-way, And turn my dark-ness in-to day, And turn my darkness in-to day.
love di-vine, He heals this wound-ed soul of mine, He heals this wound-ed soul of mine.
e'er de-fend, Up-hold and keep me to the end, Up-hold and keep me to the end.
faith-ful Guide, Find me safe sheltered by Thy side, Find me safe sheltered by Thy side.

REFRAIN.

He knows, He knows The storms that would my way op-pose;
My Fa-ther knows, I'm sure He knows that would my way op-pose;

He knows, He knows, And tempers ev-'ry wind that blows.
My Fa-ther knows, I'm sure He knows, the wind that blows.

No. 196. His Love For Me.

F. M. Eastwood.

Fred H. Byshe.

Introduction.

1. You have heard of the sto-ry of Je - sus—Of His grace, flowing boundless and free, ...
2. You have heard how He blessed lit-tle chil-dren: "Come, all ye that are weary," said He; ..
3. You have heard how the blind as they sought Him, Found their sight, when He bade them to see; ..
4. You have heard how He spake to the tem - pest—How His words, "Peace, be still!" calmed the sea;

But there's no one can tell you the full - ness Of His won-der-ful love for me. ....
So I came, and He gave me the bless - ing Of His won-der-ful love for me. ....
So my sin-blind-ed eyes have been o - pened By His won-der-ful love for me. ....
So my soul found the peace that it longed for In His won-der-ful love for me. ....

CHORUS.*

His love for me, His love for me! High as the heav'n, deep as the sea;

Love that will last thro' e - ter - ni - ty, His love for me, His love for me!

*Small notes may be used as a Soprano Obligato after last stanza.

It Is Jesus.

T. O. Chisholm.

Chas. H. Gabriel.

1. Be - hold! One com-eth in the way, In hum-ble garments clad; The poor-est of the
2. What words of grace and truth He speaks, Ne'er heard on earth before: The burdened sin-ner
3. They lead Him forth to Cal-va - ry,— O see Him bleed and die! His parch-ed lips are
4. But lo! what wondrous thing is done? The grave has lost its dead! To weep-ing ones He

poor is He, No pil-low for His head; The hun - gry, wea - ry, sick and sad In
hears that voice, And feels his sins no more; He calls the dead to life a-gain, Bids
plead-ing now For those who cru-ci - fy! His head is bowed, the cup has passed, His
re - ap-pears, When all their hopes had fled; He lin - gers but a lit - tle while, To

crowds about Him press,— To ev-'ry one He gives re-lief,—What manner of man is this?
winds and bil-lows cease,— None other man such works hath done,—What manner of man is this?
Spir - it finds re-lease,— He suf-fered thus for you and me,—What manner of man is this?
com - fort and to bless; The heav'ns receive Him from their sight,— What manner of man is this?

CHORUS.

It is Je - sus, it is Je - sus, The Man of Gal - i - lee; It is Je - sus, bless-ed

Je - sus who died on Cal-va-ry.   Introduction.   rit.   dim.

No. 198. What Would You Have Done?

Jennie E. Hussey.

Chas. H. Gabriel.

Introduction.

SOLO.

1. Had you dwelt in Beth-l'hem Cit - y When from Heav'n to earth came
2. Had you dwelt in some fair val - ley 'Mong the hills of Gal i -
3. Had your eyes be - held the scourg - ing, Pur - ple robe, and crown of
4. Had you, like the lov - ing Ma - ry, Ear - ly has - tened thro' the

down Je - sus Christ, the King of Glo - ry, Who for us left throne and
lee, When the Christ with His dis - ci - ples Walked and talked be - side the
thorn, When the un - be - liev - ers mocked Him Would you then have shared their
gloom, Would your lips have framed the ques - tion, "Who has borne Him from the

crown, Would you then, like watch - ing shep - herds, Ear - nest - ly the Child have
sea, Teach - ing les - sons from the lil - ies, How they nei - ther toil nor
scorn? Or, like quick, im - pet - uous Pe - ter, Read - y e'en with Him to
tomb?" Then what joy to hail Him ris - en, On that morn - ing fair and

sought— Would you, like the three who jour - neyed, Pre - cious gifts to Him have brought?
spin, Yet your Heav'nly Fa - ther robes them—Would your heart have let Him in?
die, O - ver - come by Sa - tan's pow - er, Just as read - y to de - ny?
bright, From the grave that could not pris - on Christ, the Lord of life and light!

No. 199. I'm a Pilgrim.

Mary S. B. Dana.

Chas. H. Gabriel.

1. I'm a pil-grim, and I'm a stran-ger; I can tar-ry but a night!
2. Of that Cit-y to which I jour-ney, My Re-deem-er is the Light;
3. There the sun-beams are ev-er shin-ing,— O my long-ing heart is there;

(1.) I can tar-ry but a night, I can tar-ry but a night!

Do not de-tain me, for I am go-ing To where the foun-tains are ev-er flow-ing;
There is no sor-row, nor an-y sigh-ing, Nor an-y tears there, nor an-y dy-ing;
Here in this coun-try, so dark and drear-y, I long have wan-dered, forlorn and wear-y;

(1.) Do not de-tain me, for I am go-ing To where the fountains are ever flow-ing;

Do not de-tain me, for I am go-ing To where the foun-tains are ev-er flow-ing.
There is no sor-row, nor an-y sigh-ing, Nor an-y tears there, nor an-y dy-ing.
Here in this coun-try, so dark and drear-y, I long have wan-dered, forlorn and wear-y.

(1.) Do not de-tain me, for I am go-ing To where the fountains are ever flow-ing.

CHORUS.

I'm a pil-grim, and I'm a stran-ger; I can tar-ry but a night;
I'm a pilgrim and a stranger, I'm a pilgrim and a stranger; I can tarry but a night, I can tarry but a night; For

I'm a pil-grim, and I'm a stran-ger, I can tar-ry, I can tar-ry but a night.
I'm a pilgrim and a stranger, I'm a pilgrim and a stranger,

No. 200. Clinging Close to His Hand.

Lizzie DeArmond.

Samuel W. Beazley.

1. As I cling to the hand of my Lord each day, .. What a
2. If I cling to His hand when the way grows dim, .. What is
3. I will cling to the hand whose nail-prints I see, .. And will

glad-ness is mine in the heav'nward way! .. Bless-ed fel-low-ship ours
there I need fear, since I trust in Him? .. For His love lights the way
rest in the love that is full and free; .. Cling-ing ev-er to Him,

all the way a-long, As my glad-ness voi-ces it-self in song. ..
that my feet must tread, And Faith's day-star bright-ens the path a-head. ..
of His grace I sing, Christ, my Sav-ior, ev-er to be my King. ..

Chorus.

Clinging, clinging by faith to my Savior's hand; Clinging, clinging to Him who my way hath planned;

Cling-ing, cling-ing to Je-sus, my Hope, my All; Cling-ing, clinging, clinging, I can-not fall.

J-13

No. 201. Oh, It Is Wonderful!

C. H. G.

Chas. H. Gabriel.

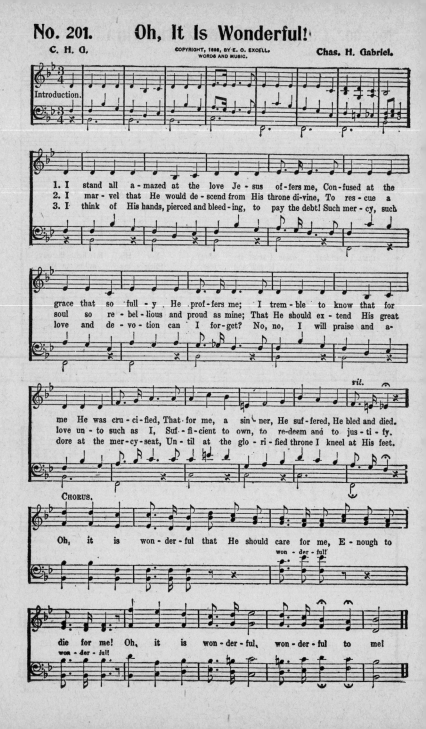

Introduction.

1. I stand all a-mazed at the love Je-sus of-fers me, Con-fused at the
2. I mar-vel that He would de-scend from His throne di-vine, To res-cue a
3. I think of His hands, pierced and bleed-ing, to pay the debt! Such mer-cy, such

grace that so full-y He prof-fers me; I trem-ble to know that for
soul so re-bel-lious and proud as mine; That He should ex-tend His great
love and de-vo-tion can I for-get? No, no, I will praise and a-

me He was cru-ci-fied, That for me, a sin-ner, He suf-fered, He bled and died.
love un-to such as I, Suf-fi-cient to own, to re-deem and to jus-ti-fy.
dore at the mer-cy-seat, Un-til at the glo-ri-fied throne I kneel at His feet.

CHORUS.

Oh, it is won-der-ful that He should care for me, E-nough to
won-der-full

die for me! Oh, it is won-der-ful, won-der-ful to me!
won-der-full

No. 202.　Reapers Are Needed.

Lizzie DeArmond.

Samuel W. Beazley.

1. Hark to the mu-sic re-sound-ing, Reap-ers are need-ed to-day; Fields are all
2. For-ward with hearts full of glad-ness, Reap-ers, I pray you, make haste; Grain there is
3. Hark to the song they are sing-ing! See, they have treas-ures so rare; Soon will the

white, to the har-vest Let us be up and a-way! Ev-er the Mas-ter is
read-y and wait-ing, If not soon gath-ered, will waste; Then let us hear you re-
har-vest be end-ed, Haste, then, their tro-phies to share. Let no one be i-dly

call-ing, Has-ten! the shad-ows are fall-ing; On to the har-vest-field, Gath-er the
ply-ing, La-bor with cour-age un-dy-ing, Send up a word of cheer, Tell of the
dream-ing, Look! look! the har-vest is gleam-ing, Join ye the reap-ing band, Lend them a

Chorus or Quartet.

gold-en yield, Pre-cious sheaves.
rest so near, Rest at home.　Hark! hark! comes the song, On! on! join the throng;
help-ing hand, Ere the night.

Forth with joy-ful, lov-ing heart, Bravely do your part; Hark! hark! rings the call; Haste! haste!

one and all; On where the har-vest stands, Waiting for will-ing hands Souls to win.

No. 203. No Room In the Inn.

A. L. Skilton.

E. Grace Updegraff.

1. No beautiful cham-ber, No soft cradle bed, No place but a man-ger,
2. No sweet con-se-cra-tion, No seeking His part, No hu-mil-i-a-tion,
3. No one to re-ceive Him, No welcome while here, No balm to re-lieve Him,

No-where for His head; No prais-es of glad-ness, No tho't of their sin,
No place in the heart; No tho't of the Sav-ior, No sorrow for sin,
No staff but a spear; No seeking His treasure, No weeping for sin,

CHORUS.

No glo-ry but sad-ness, No room in the inn.
No prayer for His fa-vor, No room in the inn. No room, no room for Jesus, Oh,
No doing His pleas-ure, No room in the inn.

rit.

Lest you should hear at Heaven's gate,
give Him welcome free, "There is no room for thee."

No. 204. Raise Me, Jesus, to Thy Bosom.

Geo. Birdseye.

Wm. A. Huntley.

* Use small notes in Duet.

1. Raise me, Je-sus, to Thy bos-om, From this world.... of sin and woes;
2. Raise me, Je-sus, to Thy bos-om, For my heart.... is slave to fear,
3. Raise me, Je-sus, to Thy bos-om, Hear a con - trite spirit's prayer;

D.C.—*Raise me, Je-sus, to Thy bos-om, From this world.... of sin and woes;*

Let me feel Thine arms a-round me, Then my soul may know re-pose.
That will van-ish as a shad-ow, When it feels Thy presence near.
Raise me from the sin a-round me, Ere I yield me to de-spair.
Let me feel Thine arms a-round me, Then my soul may know re-pose.

Solo.

I am weary with my bur-den, And I come to Thee for rest; Kneeling
In my anguish deign to hear me All my sin and grief con-fess; By the
Oh, I feel that Thou wilt hear me, And will give me ho - ly rest; Now I

D. C. Quartet or Chorus.

at Thy feet, I pray Thee Lift me, Je - sus, to Thy breast.....
prom-ise Thou hast giv - en, Lift me, Je - sus, to Thy breast.....
feel Thy glo - ry near me, Lift me, Je - sus, to Thy breast.....

* Use the stanzas as Duet and Solo; the D. C. as Quartet or Chorus.

No. 205. Sometime, Somewhere.

Mrs. Ophelia G. Adams.

Charlie D. Tillman.

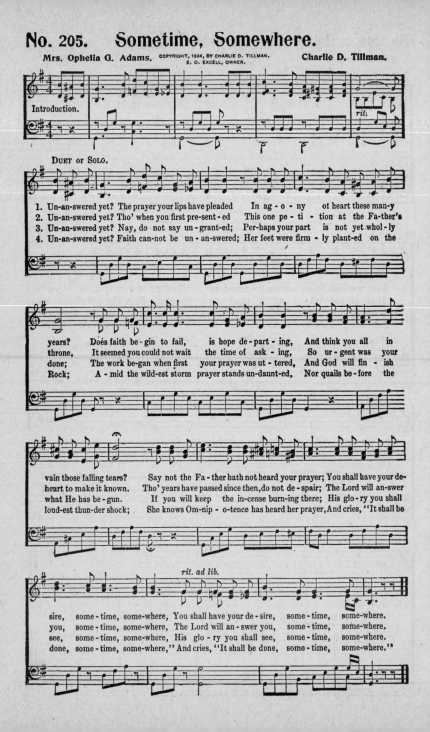

Introduction. *rit.*

DUET or SOLO.

1. Un-an-swered yet? The prayer your lips have pleaded In ag - o - ny of heart these man-y
2. Un-an-swered yet? Tho' when you first present - ed This one pe - ti - tion at the Fa-ther's
3. Un-an-swered yet? Nay, do not say un - grant-ed; Per-haps your part is not yet whol-ly
4. Un-an-swered yet? Faith can-not be un - an-swered; Her feet were firm - ly plant-ed on the

years? Does faith be - gin to fail, is hope de - part - ing, And think you all in
throne, It seemed you could not wait the time of ask - ing, So ur - gent was your
done; The work be-gan when first your prayer was ut - tered, And God will fin - ish
Rock; A - mid the wild-est storm prayer stands un-daunt-ed, Nor quails be - fore the

vain those falling tears? Say not the Fa - ther hath not heard your prayer; You shall have your de-
heart to make it known. Tho' years have passed since then, do not de - spair; The Lord will an-swer
what He has be - gun. If you will keep the in-cense burn-ing there; His glo - ry you shall
loud-est thun-der shock; She knows Om-nip - o-tence has heard her prayer, And cries, "It shall be

rit. ad lib.

sire, some - time, some-where, You shall have your de - sire, some - time, some-where.
you, some - time, some-where, The Lord will an - swer you, some - time, some-where.
see, some - time, some-where, His glo - ry you shall see, some - time, some-where.
done, some - time, some-where," And cries, "It shall be done, some - time, some-where."

No. 206. How Sweet is His Love.

James Rowe.

E. O. Excell.

Introduction.

1. When troub-led my soul, and when peace I would find, How sweet is the love of Je-sus! ..
2. When faint-ing and help-less I fall in de-spair, How sweet is the love of Je-sus! ..
3. When dark is the night, and when sore-ly distressed, How sweet is the love of Je-sus! ..

When lone-ly I feel, and when friends are un-kind, How sweet is His love to me! ...
When suf-f'ring with pain, and when sor-row I bear, How sweet is His love to me! ...
When long-ing my soul for His com-fort and rest, How sweet is His love to me! ...

Chorus.

O ... how sweet, O how sweet is His love, .. How sweet is His love to

me! .. When friends all have gone, and I suf-fer a-lone, How sweet is His love to me! ..

No. 207. The Sinner and the Song.

W. L. T.
Will L. Thompson.

COPYRIGHT, 1904, BY WILL L. THOMPSON.
HOPE PUBLISHING CO. OWNERS.

Solo.

Organ.

1. A sin-ner was wand'ring at e-ven-tide, His tempter was watching close by at his side,
2. He stopped and listened to ev-'ry sweet chord, He remember'd the time he once loved the Lord,

In his heart raged a battle for right against wrong, But hark! from the church he hears the sweet song;
Come on! says the tempter, come, on with the throng, But hark! from the church a-gain swells the song,

pp Quartet.
Solo.
Organ.

1. Je-sus, lov-er of my soul, Let me to Thy bo-som fly, Oh, tempter, de-part,
2. While the bil-lows near me roll, while the tem-pest still is high,

I have served thee too long, I fly to the Sav-ior, He dwells in that song, O Lord,

can it be that a sin-ner like me, May find a sweet ref-uge by com-ing to Thee?

pp Quartet.
Solo.
Organ.

Oth-er ref-uge have I none; Hangs my help-less soul on Thee. I come, Lord, I

pp Quartet.

come, Thou'lt for-give the dark past, And O, re-ceive my soul at last.

No. 208. My Mother's Song.

COPYRIGHT, 1908, BY E. O. EXCELL.
WORDS AND MUSIC.

J. E. Ramsey.

E. O. Excell.

1. Sing me the song my moth-er sang In ac-cents sweet and low, That dear old song she
2. O sing it as she sang that day, So tender and so sweet, When pen - i - tent I
3. Sing me the dear old song a-gain, It brings a sweet re - lief; 'Twas mother's song in
4. Sing as she sang, with faith so strong, When called by an - gel band, To join her song with

sang to me In childhood long a - go; Me thinks I hear her voice a-gain, And
knelt to pray, Be - fore the mer - cy - seat; It seemed a song from angel tongue, My
joy or pain, Her balm for ev - 'ry grief; In vale or on the mountain steep, She
ser-aph throng, In heav'n's sweet sum-mer land; Still sing-ing God's re-deem-ing love, His

see her smil - ing face, As when she sang that sweet re-fraih .Of God's A-maz - ing Grace.
bro-ken heart to bless, When mother sang that dear old song Of God's A-maz - ing Grace.
sang her song of praise,—The Lord my soul will safe-ly keep, Thro' His A-maz - ing Grace.
glo - ry on her face, She winged her way to realms a-bove,Thro' God's A-maz - ing Grace.

After each stanza sing the corresponding stanza of the following hymn: "Amazing Grace."

No. 209. Amazing Grace.

John Newton.

Arr. by E. O. Excell.

1. { Amazing grace! how sweet the sound,
That saved a wretch like me! I once was lost,but now am found,Was blind, but now I see.

2 'Twas grace that taught my heart
And grace my fears relieved; [to fear
How precious did that grace appear
The hour I first believed!

3 Thro' many dangers, toils and
I have already come; [snares,
'Tis grace hath bro't me safe thus
And grace will lead me home.[far,

4 When we've been there ten thou-
Bright shining as the sun,[sand years
We've no less days to sing God's
Than when we first begun. [praise

Awakening Chorus.

Charlotte G. Homer   Chas. H. Gabriel.

1. A-wake! a-wake! and sing the bless-ed sto-ry; A-
   A-wake!   a-wake!
2. Ring out! ring out! O bells of joy and glad-ness! Re-
   Ring out!   ring out!

wake! a-wake! and let your song of praise a-rise; A-wake! a-
  A-wake!   a-wake!   A-wake!
peat, re-peat a-new the sto-ry o'er a-gain, Till all the
  Re-peat,   re-peat,   Till all

wake! the earth is full of glo-ry, And light is beam-ing
  a-wake!   And light   is beam-ing
earth shall lose its weight of sad-ness, And shout a-new the
  the earth.   And shout   a-new

MALE VOICES IN UNISON.

from the ra-diant skies; The rocks and rills, the vales and hills re-sound with
glo-ri-ous re-frain; With an-gels in the heights sing of the great sal-

FULL HARMONY.

glad-ness, All na-ture joins to sing the triumph song. The Lord Je-
va-tion He wrest-ed from the hand of sin and death.

Awakening Chorus.

ho - vah reigns and sin is back-ward hurled! Re-joice! re-
sin is back-ward hurled!

joice! lift heart and voice, Je - ho - vah reigns!

FULL HARMONY.

Pro-claim His sov-'reign pow'r to all the world, And let His
pow'r to all the world, And let the

glo - rious ban-ner be un-furled! Je - ho - vah reigns!
grand and glo-rious ban-ner be un-furled! Je-ho-vah reigns! Je-ho-vah reigns!

Re - joice! re - joice! re - joice! Je - ho - vah reigns!
Re - joice! re - joice! re - joice!

No. 211. O How I Love Him.

Rev. A. H. Ackley.

B. D. Ackley.

INTRODUCTION.

rit.

1. At Cal-v'ry's cross I met a Friend,....
2. When I am help-less and a-lone,......
3. And when the Light of Heav-en fills.......

Who touched my bro-ken heart,...
'Tis then I seek this Guide;..
My soul with fair-est day,....

My guilt-y soul re-vived, made whole,....
So true and kind I al-ways find......
I know that He is with me still,......

O How I Love Him.

Thro' grace set me a - part. . .
Him wait - ing at my side. . .
And will be all the way. . .

CHORUS.

O how I love Him, The Man of Gal - i - lee! . . .
O how I love Him, The Man of Gal - i - lee!

O how I love Him, Who died on Cal - va - ry! . . .
O how I love Him, Who died on Cal - va - ry!

There is no oth - er Such a Friend or Broth - er;

O how I love Him, Be - cause He died for me! . .

Crown Him King of Kings.

E. E. Rexford.

DeLoss Smith.

INTRODUCTION.

VOICES IN UNISON.

1. Crown Him, crown Him with glo-ry the King of kings;
2. He who reigns o'er the king-doms of earth to-day,
3. Praise Him, praise Him, the King on the great white throne;

Praise and hom-age each heart as its trib-ute brings;
Sends His bless-ings to those in the heav'n-ward way;
Love Him, serve Him, who rul-eth by love a-lone;

Sing, O earth, and u-nite in the might-y re-frain—
Sing we prais-es with hearts that with love o-ver-flow—
Up to heav-en the shout of the glo-ri-fied rings—

Crown Him King of Kings.

Christ, our Re-deem-er and King, will for-ev-er reign!
Glo-ry to Je-sus who con-quers our ev-'ry foe!
Laud and a-dore Him, and crown Him the King of kings!

CHORUS.

Sing ho-san-nas, loud let the joy-ful an-thems ring,

Laud and wor-ship Him whom the an-gels a-dore!

Crown Him, crown Him, Sav-ior, Re-deem-er and King,

Glo-ry to God in the high-est— Glo-ry for-ev-er-more!

No. 213.   All Hail, Immanuel!

D. R. Van Sickle.

Chas. H. Gabriel.

1. All hail to Thee, Im-man-u-el, We cast.......our crowns be-
2. All hail to Thee, Im-man-u-el, The ran - - somed hosts sur-
3. All hail to Thee, Im-man-u-el, Our ris - - en King and

fore Thee; Let ev-'ry heart o-bey Thy will, And ev - - 'ry voice a-
round Thee; And earthly monarchs clamor forth Their Sov - 'reign, King to
Sav - ior! Thy foes are vanquished, and Thou art Om-nip - o-tent for-

dore Thee. In praise to Thee, our Sav - ior, King, The vi-brant chords of
crown Thee. While those redeemed in a - ges gone, As-sem-bled round the
ev - er. Death, sin and hell no lon - ger reign, And Sa-tan's pow'r is

heav - en ring, And ech - o back the might-y strain: All
great white throne, Break forth in - to im - mor - tal song: All
burst in twain; E - ter - nal glo - ry to Thy Name: All

hail!   all hail!   All hail, all hail, Im-man-u-el!
All hail!   all hail!

All Hail, Immanuel!

CHORUS.

Hail, ... Im-man-u-el, Im-man-u-el! Hail, ...

Hail to the King we love so well, Hail, Im-man-u-el! Hail to the King we love so well.
Hail! . . . .

Im-man-u-el, Im-man-u-el!

Hail, Im-man-u-el! Glo-ry and hon-or and maj-es-ty,
Hail! . . . . Glo-ry and maj-es-ty.

Wis-dom and pow-er be un-to Thee, Now and ev-er-more!
Wis-dom be un-to Thee,

Hail, ... Im-man-u-el, Im-man-u-el! Hail, ...

Hail to the King we love so well, Hail, Im-man-u-el! Hail to the King we love so well.
Hail! . . . .

Im-man-u-el, Im-man-u-el!

Hail, Im-man-u-el! King of kings and Lord of lords, All hail, Im-man-u-el!
Hail! . . . .

J-14

No. 214.   Draw Nigh, Immanuel.

Charlotte G. Homer.

Chas. H. Gabriel.

f INTRO.

1. Draw nigh to us, O God of hosts, And fill us to the ut-ter-most
2. Draw nigh to us, O Might-y One! Our shel-ter be from sun to sun;
3. Draw nigh to us, Im-man-u-el, Thou Mighty God of Is-ra-el!

With zeal to work for Thee to-day, In Thine all-wise ap-point-ed way;
Our Al-pha and O-me-ga Thou Be-fore whom ev-'ry knee shall bow;
Once more from Si-nai's flam-ing height Speak, that we may be led a-right;

Re-veal Thy will in us, and show Thy hand di-vine, that we may know
De-liv-er us from ev-'ry sin; In us a might-y work be-gin;
Al-might-y, ev-er-last-ing King of kings, with contrite hearts we sing,

We are Thy children, Thou our Guide And hid-ing-place, what-e'er be-tide.
In-crease our faith, our strength renew, Fit us a might-y work to do.
The righteous maj-es-ty and love Of Him who built the heav'ns a-bove.

Draw Nigh, Immanuel.

CHORUS.

Draw nigh, draw nigh, Im - man - u - el, In
Draw nigh, draw nigh, Draw nigh, Im - man - u - el,

grandeur and in maj - es - ty re - veal Thyself to-day; Re - joice, re-

joice, O Is - ra - el, Thy God Omnipotent shall reign with

u - ni-ver-sal sway: In grandeur and in maj - es - ty re - veal Thyself to-

day; Thy God Om-nip - o - tent shall reign with u - ni - ver - sal sway.

No. 215.   A Song of Victory.

Charlotte G. Homer.

Chas. H. Gabriel.

1. Loud - ly   un - to the world is   a cho - rus re-sound - ing,
2. Press - ing   on to the bat - tle, each sol - dier re - joi - ces,
3. Glo - ry!   glo - ry to God in the high - est for - ev - er!

From the hosts of the Lord as they march a - long,
Sing - ing joy - ful - ly un - to the gra - cious King;
For the King in His beau - ty shall yet ap - pear;

Rich in har - mo - ny, send-ing the ech - oes re - bound - ing,
Earth is join - ing her praise with the tu - mult of voi - ces,
Shout a - loud, for Je - ho - vah, our God, will de - liv - er;

Swell - ing might - i - ly from the vic - to - rious throng.
While the arch - es of Heav - en with mu - sic ring.
His the bat - tle, and vic - to - ry draw - eth near.

A Song of Victory.

CHORUS.

Vic - to-ry! rings aloud the bat-tle-cry, bat-tle-cry! Till the glad
Vic - to-ry! vic-to - ry! rings a-loud the bat - tle-cry, . . Un-til the glo-ri-ous

echoes reach the vaulted sky, vaulted sky; O'er the world be un-furled
ech - oes reach the vault - ed sky; . . O - ver the world now be un-furled His

now His flag from shore to shore; Loy - al, true, in the ranks each
flag from shore to shore; . . Loy-al and true, in the ranks each faith - ful

soldier stands, bravely stands, Glad-ly His will o-bey-ing in what-e'er
sol - - dier stands, . . Glad-ly o - bey-ing in what-so-ev - er He . . com-

He commands; He the King, the kingdom His for - ev - er - more.
mands; . . He is the King, and the king-dom His for - ev - er - more.

No. 216. The Old Book and the Old Faith.

G. H. C.   COPYRIGHT, 1914, BY W. E. M. HACKLEMAN.   Geo. H. Carr.

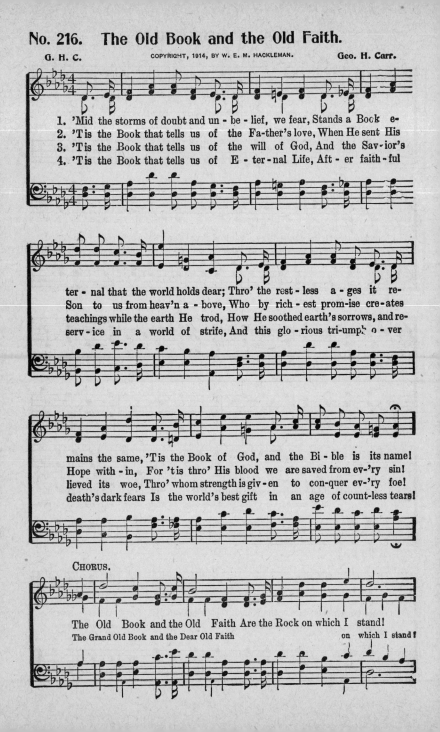

1. 'Mid the storms of doubt and un - be - lief, we fear, Stands a Book e-
2. 'Tis the Book that tells us of the Fa - ther's love, When He sent His
3. 'Tis the Book that tells us of the will of God, And the Sav - ior's
4. 'Tis the Book that tells us of E - ter - nal Life, Aft - er faith - ful

ter - nal that the world holds dear; Thro' the rest - less a - ges it re-
Son to us from heav'n a - bove, Who by rich - est prom - ise cre - ates
teachings while the earth He trod, How He soothed earth's sorrows, and re-
serv - ice in a world of strife, And this glo - rious tri - umph o - ver

mains the same, 'Tis the Book of God, and the Bi - ble is its name!
Hope with - in, For 'tis thro' His blood we are saved from ev - 'ry sin!
lieved its woe, Thro' whom strength is giv - en to con - quer ev - 'ry foe!
death's dark fears Is the world's best gift in an age of count - less tears!

CHORUS.

The Old Book and the Old Faith Are the Rock on which I stand!

The Grand Old Book and the Dear Old Faith   on which I stand!

The Old Book and the Old Faith.

The Old Book and the Old Faith Are the bul-wark of the land! ...
The Grand Old Book and the Dear Old Faith

Thro' storm and stress they stand the test, In ev.-'ry clime and na-tion blest;

The Old Book and the Old Faith Are the Hope of ev-'ry land!
The Grand Old Book and the Dear Old Faith

GRAND CHORUS AT CLOSE. *(May be omitted.)*

Oh, the Grand Old Book and the Dear Old Faith Are the Rock on which I stand!

rit.

Oh, the Grand Old Book and the Dear Old Faith Are the Hope of ev-'ry land!

Rock of Ages.

A. M. Toplady.

E. O. Excell.

1. Rock .. of A — ges, cleft .. for me,
2. Could .. my tears .. for - ev — er flow,
3. While .. I draw .. this fleet — ing breath,

1. Rock of A — ges, cleft for me, Blest Rock of A — ges, cleft for me,
2. Could my tears for - ev — er flow, Oh! Could my tears for - ev - er flow,
3. While I draw this fleet-ing breath, Yes, While I draw this fleet-ing breath,

Let .. me hide .. my - self .. in Thee;
Could .. my zeal .. no lan — — guor know,
When .. mine eyes .. shall close .. in death,

Let me hide my - self in Thee, Oh! Let me hide my - self in Thee;
Could my zeal no lan-guor know, Oh! Could my zeal no lan-guor know,
When mine eyes shall close in death, Yes, When mine eyes shall close in death,

Let .. the wa — — ter and .. the blood,
These .. for sin .. could not .. a - tone;
When .. I rise .. to worlds .. un - known,

Let the wa - ter and the blood, Oh! Let the wa - ter and the blood,
These for sin could not a - tone, No, These for sin could not a - tone:
When I rise to worlds un-known, Yes, When I rise to worlds un-known,

Rock of Ages.

From .. Thy wound - ed side .. which flowed,
Thou .. must save .. and Thou .. a - lone;
And .. be - hold .. Thee on ... Thy throne,

From Thy wound-ed side which flowed, Yes, From Thy wound-ed side which flowed,
Thou must save and Thou a-lone, Yes, Thou must save and Thou a-lone;
And be-hold Thee on Thy throne, Yes, And be-hold Thee on Thy throne,

Be .. of sin .. the doub - le cure,
In .. my hand .. no price .. I bring;
Rock .. of A - ges, cleft .. for me,

Be of sin the doub-le cure, Yes, Be of sin the doub-le cure,
In my hand no price I bring, Lord, In my hand no price I bring;
Rock of A - ges, cleft for me, Blest Rock of A - ges, cleft for me,

rit.

Repeat pp.

Save ... from wrath .. and make .. me pure.
Sim - - ply to ... Thy cross ... I cling.
Let ... me hide .. my - self ... in Thee.

Repeat pp.

Save from wrath and make me pure, Yes, Save from wrath and make me pure.
Sim - ply to Thy cross I cling, Lord, Sim - ply to Thy cross I cling.
Let me hide my - self in Thee, Oh, Let me hide my - self in Thee.

No. 218. Reapers Are Needed.

C. H. G.

Chas. H. Gabriel.

1. Standing in the mar-ket pla-ces all the sea-son thro', I - dly say-ing,
2. Ev - 'ry sheaf you gath-er will be-come a jew - el bright In the crown you
3. Morning hours are pass-ing and the eve-ning fol-lows fast; Soon the time of

"Lord, is there no work that I can do?" O how man-y loi - ter, while the
hope to wear in yon-der world of light; Seek the gems im-mor - tal that are
reap - ing will for-ev - er-more be past; Emp-ty-hand-ed to the Mas-ter

Mas - ter calls a - new, "Reapers! reap-ers! Who will work to-day?"
pre - cious in his sight! "Reapers! reap-ers! Who will work to-day?"
will you go at last? "Reapers! reap-ers! Who will work to-day?"

CHORUS.

Lift thine eyes and look up - on the fields that stand
Lift thine eyes and look up - on the fields that stand all read - y,

Lift thine eyes to fields that stand all

Ripe and read - y for the will - ing gleaner's hand,
Ripe and read - y for the will - ing gleaner's hand, O rouse ye,

Read - y for the glean - er's hand, O

Reapers Are Needed.

Rouse ye, O sleep-ers! Ye are need-ed as reapers! Who will be the first to

answer, "Master, here am I"?
quickly, "Master, here am I"?

Far and wide the ripened
Far and wide the rip - ened

O answer! Far and wide the

grain is bend-ing low, In the breez - es gen - tly
grain is bend-ing low, In breez-es, In the breez-es gen - tly

grain bends low, and In the breeze waves

wav - ing to and fro, Rouse ye, O sleep-ers, Ye are need-ed as
wav - ing to and fro, O rouse ye,

to and fro, O

reap-ers, And the gold - en har-vest days are swift - ly pass-ing by.

No. 219. All Hail the Power of Jesus' Name.

E. Perronet.   USED BY PERMISSION.

1. All hail the pow'r of Je-sus' name! Let an-gels prostrate fall,
2. Ye cho-sen seed of Is-rael's race, Ye ransomed from the fall,
3. Let ev-'ry kin-dred, ev-'ry tribe, On this ter-res-trial ball,
4. O that with yon-der sa-cred throng We at His feet may fall,

Let an-gels pros-trate fall; Bring forth the roy-al di-a-dem,
Ye ransomed from the fall, Hail Him who saves you by His grace,
On this ter-res-trial ball, To Him all maj-es-ty as-cribe,
We at His feet may fall! We'll join the ev-er-last-ing song,

And crown . . . . Him, Crown Him,
And crown Him, crown Him, crown Him, crown Him, And crown Him Lord of
And crown . . . . Him, Crown Him,

And crown Him, crown Him, crown Him, Crown . . . .
crown Him, crown Him;

crown Him, crown Him;
all, crown Him; And crown Him Lord of all!
crown . . . . . Him;

. . . . Him; And crown Him Lord of all!

DEVOTIONAL HYMNS

O Zion, Haste.

James Walch.

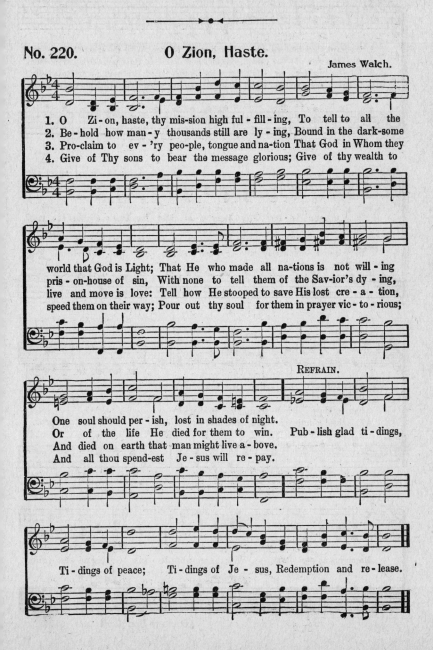

1. O   Zi-on, haste, thy mis-sion high ful-fill-ing, To   tell to all   the
2. Be-hold how man-y thousands still are ly-ing, Bound in the dark-some
3. Pro-claim to ev-'ry peo-ple, tongue and na-tion That God in Whom they
4. Give of Thy sons to bear the message glorious; Give of thy wealth to

world that God is Light; That He who made all na-tions is not will-ing
pris-on-house of sin, With none to tell them of the Sav-ior's dy-ing,
live and move is love: Tell how He stooped to save His lost cre-a-tion,
speed them on their way; Pour out thy soul for them in prayer vic-to-rious;

REFRAIN.

One soul should per-ish, lost in shades of night.
Or   of the life He died for them to win.   Pub-lish glad ti-dings,
And   died on earth that man might live a-bove.
And   all thou spend-est Je-sus will re-pay.

Ti-dings of peace;   Ti-dings of Je-sus, Redemption and re-lease.

No. 221. Onward, Christian Soldiers.

Sabine Baring-Gould.

Arthur Sullivan.

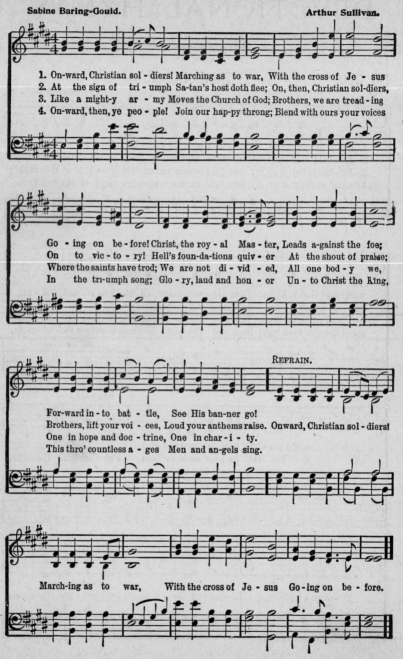

1. On-ward, Christian sol - diers! Marching as to war, With the cross of Je - sus
2. At the sign of tri - umph Sa-tan's host doth flee; On, then, Christian sol-diers,
3. Like a might-y ar - my Moves the Church of God; Brothers, we are tread - ing
4. On-ward, then, ye peo - ple! Join our hap-py throng; Blend with ours your voices

Go - ing on be - fore! Christ, the roy - al Mas - ter, Leads a-gainst the foe;
On to vic - to - ry! Hell's foun-da-tions quiv - er At the shout of praise;
Where the saints have trod; We are not di - vid - ed, All one bod - y we,
In the tri-umph song; Glo - ry, laud and hon - or Un - to Christ the King,

Refrain.

For-ward in - to bat - tle, See His ban-ner go!
Brothers, lift your voi - ces, Loud your anthems raise. Onward, Christian sol - diers!
One in hope and doc - trine, One in char - i - ty.
This thro' countless a - ges Men and an-gels sing.

March-ing as to war, With the cross of Je - sus Go-ing on be - fore.

No. 222. It Came Upon the Midnight Clear.

E. H. Sears.   R. Storrs Willis.

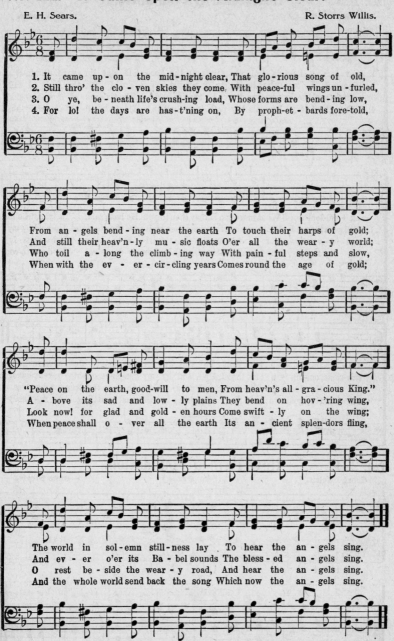

1. It came up-on the mid-night clear, That glo-rious song of old,
2. Still thro' the clo-ven skies they come, With peace-ful wings un-furled,
3. O ye, be-neath life's crush-ing load, Whose forms are bend-ing low,
4. For lo! the days are has-t'ning on, By proph-et-bards fore-told,

From an-gels bend-ing near the earth To touch their harps of gold;
And still their heav'n-ly mu-sic floats O'er all the wear-y world;
Who toil a-long the climb-ing way With pain-ful steps and slow,
When with the ev-er-cir-cling years Comes round the age of gold;

"Peace on the earth, good-will to men, From heav'n's all-gra-cious King."
A-bove its sad and low-ly plains They bend on hov-'ring wing,
Look now! for glad and gold-en hours Come swift-ly on the wing;
When peace shall o-ver all the earth Its an-cient splen-dors fling,

The world in sol-emn still-ness lay To hear the an-gels sing.
And ev-er o'er its Ba-bel sounds The bless-ed an-gels sing.
O rest be-side the wear-y road, And hear the an-gels sing.
And the whole world send back the song Which now the an-gels sing.

How Firm a Foundation.

George Keith.   Unknown.

1. How firm a foun-da-tion, ye saints of the Lord, Is laid for your faith in His
2. "Fear not, I am with thee, O be not dis-mayed, For I am thy God, I will
3. "When thro' the deep waters I call thee to go, The riv-ers of sor-row shall
4. "When thro' fiery tri-als thy path-way shall lie, My grace, all-suf-fi-cient, shall

ex - cel-lent word! What more can He say than to you He hath said, To you, who for
still give thee aid; I'll strengthen thee, help thee, and cause thee to stand, Up-held by my
not o-ver-flow; For I will be with thee thy tri-als to bless, And sanc-ti-fy
be thy sup-ply, The flames shall not hurt thee; I on-ly de - sign Thy dross to con-

ref - uge to Je - sus have fled? To you, who for ref - uge to Je - sus have fled?
gra-cious, om-nip - o-tent hand, Up-held by my gra-cious, om-nip-o-tent hand.
to thee thy deep-est dis-tress, And sanc-ti-fy to thee thy deep-est dis-tress.
sume, and thy gold to re-fine, Thy dross to con-sume, and thy gold to re-fine."

No. 224.

How Firm a Foundation.

George Keith.   (Second tune.)   Anne Steele.

Refuge.

Charles Wesley.

J. P. Holbrook.

1. Je - sus, Lov - er of my soul, Let me to Thy bos - om fly, While the
2. Oth - er ref - uge have I none; Hangs my help-less soul on Thee; Leave, oh,
3. Thou, O Christ, art all I want; More than all in Thee I find; Raise the

near - er wa - ters roll, While the tem - pest still is high. Hide me, O, my
leave me not a - lone, Still sup - port and com-fort me. All my trust on
fall - en, cheer the faint, Heal the sick, and lead the blind. Just and ho - ly

Sav - ior, hide, Till the storm of life is past; Safe in - to the ha - ven
Thee is stayed; All my help from Thee I bring; Cov - er my de - fense-less
is Thy name, I am all un-right-eous-ness; Vile and full of sin I

guide, O re-ceive my soul at last!
head With the shad-ow of Thy wing.
am, Thou art full of truth and grace.

4 Plenteous grace with Thee is found,
    Grace to cover all my sin;
Let the healing streams abound;
    Make and keep me pure within.
Thou of life the fountain art,
    Freely let me take of Thee;
Spring Thou up within my heart,
    Rise to all eternity.

No. 226. **Jesus, Lover of My Soul.**

S. B. Marsh.

FINE.

D. C.

15

No. 227. Sun of My Soul.

John Keble.

Peter Ritter.

1. Sun of my soul, Thou Sav - ior dear, It is not night if Thou be near;
2. When the soft dews of kind - ly sleep My wear-ied eye - lids gen - tly steep,
3. A - bide with me from morn till eve, For with-out Thee I can - not live;
4. Come near and bless us when we wake, Ere thro' the world our way we take;

Oh, may no earth - born cloud a - rise To hide Thee from Thy ser-vant's eyes.
Be my last tho't, how sweet to rest For-ev - er on my Sav - ior's breast.
A - bide with me when night is nigh, For without Thee I dare not die.
Till, in the o - cean of Thy love, We lose our-selves in heav'n a - bove.

No. 228. Jesus Shall Reign.

Isaac Watts.

John Hatton.

1. Je - sus shall reign wher-e'er the sun Does His suc-ces-sive jour - neys run;
2. From north to south the princ - es meet, To pay their homage at His feet;
3. To Him shall end - less prayer be made, And end - less prais-es crown His head;
4. Peo - ple and realms of ev - 'ry tongue Dwell on His love with sweet - est song,

His king-dom spread from shore to shore, Till moons shall wax and wane no more.
While western em - pires own their Lord, And sav - age tribes at - tend His word.
His name like sweet per-fume shall rise With ev - 'ry morn - ing sac - ri - fice.
And in - fant voi - ces shall pro - claim Their ear - ly bless - ings on His name.

No. 229. Come, Thou Almighty King.

Charles Wesley.

Felice Giardini.

1. Come, Thou Al-might-y King, Help us Thy name to sing, Help us to praise: Fa-ther all-
2. Come, Thou in-car-nate Word, Gird on Thy mighty sword, Our prayer attend; Come, and Thy
3. Come, ho-ly Com-fort-er, Thy sa-cred wit-ness bear In this glad hour; Thou who al-
4. To the great One in Three, The highest prais-es be Hence, ev-er-more! His sov'reign

glo-ri-ous, O'er all vic-to-ri-ous, Come, and reign o-ver us, An-cient of days!
peo-ple bless, And give Thy word success: Spir-it of ho-li-ness, On us de-scend!
might-y art, Now rule in ev-'ry heart, And ne'er from us de-part, Spir-it of pow'r!
maj-es-ty May we in glo-ry see, And to e-ter-ni-ty Love and a-dore!

No. 230. Break Thou the Bread of Life.

Mary Ann Lathbury.

William F. Sherwin.

1. Break Thou the bread of life, Dear Lord, to me, As Thou didst break the loaves Beside the sea.
2. Bless Thou the truth, dear Lord, To me, to me, As Thou didst bless the bread By Gal-i-lee;
3. Teach me to live, dear Lord, On-ly for Thee, As Thy dis-ci-ples lived In Gal-i-lee;

Be-yond the sacred page I seek Thee, Lord; My spir-it pants for Thee, O liv-ing Word!
Then shall all bondage cease, All fet-ters fall, And I shall find my peace, My all in all.
Then, all my struggles o'er, Then, vict'ry won, I shall behold Thee, Lord, The living one.

No. 231. Holy Ghost, With Light Divine.

A. Reed.

Gottschalk.

1. Ho - ly Ghost, with light di - vine, Shine up - on this heart of mine;
2. Ho - ly Ghost, with pow'r di - vine, Cleanse this guilt - y heart of mine;
3. Ho - ly Ghost, with joy di - vine, Cheer this sad - dened heart of mine;
4. Ho - ly Spir - it, all di - vine, Dwell with - in this heart of mine;

Chase the shades of night a - way, Turn my dark - ness in - to day.
Long hath sin with - out con - trol, Held do - min - ion o'er my soul.
Bid my man - y woes de - part, Heal my wound - ed, bleed - ing heart.
Cast down ev - 'ry i - dol - throne, Reign su - preme—and reign a - lone.

No. 232. Jesus, Savior, Pilot Me.

Edward Hopper.

J. E. Gould.

FINE.

1. Je - sus, Sav - ior, pi - lot me O - ver life's tem - pes - tuous sea:
D. C.—Chart and com - pass come from Thee, Je - sus, Sav - ior, pi - lot me.

D. C.

Un - known waves be - fore me roll, Hid - ing rocks and treach'rous shoal;

2 As a mother stills her child,
Thou canst hush the ocean wild;
Boisterous waves obey Thy will
When Thou say'st to them "Be still!"
Wondrous Sovereign of the sea,
Jesus, Savior, pilot me.

3 When at last I near the shore,
And the fearful breakers roar
'Twixt me and the peaceful rest,
Then, while leaning on Thy breast,
May I hear Thee say to me.
"Fear not, I will pilot thee."

No. 233. My Faith Looks Up to Thee.

Ray Palmer.   **Lowell Mason.**

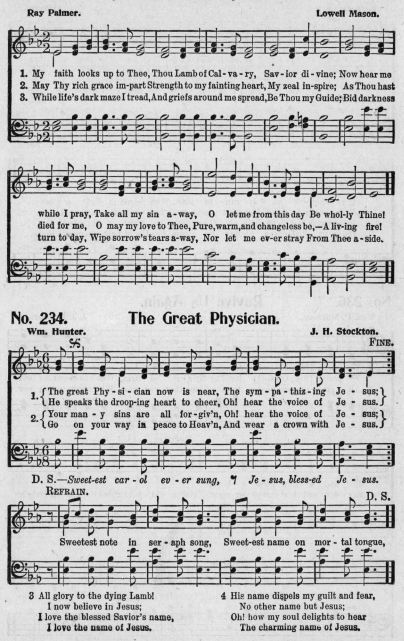

1. My faith looks up to Thee, Thou Lamb of Cal-va-ry, Sav-ior di-vine; Now hear me
2. May Thy rich grace im-part Strength to my fainting heart, My zeal in-spire; As Thou hast
3. While life's dark maze I tread, And griefs around me spread, Be Thou my Guide; Bid darkness

while I pray, Take all my sin a-way, O let me from this day Be whol-ly Thine!
died for me, O may my love to Thee, Pure, warm, and changeless be,—A liv-ing fire!
turn to day, Wipe sorrow's tears a-way, Nor let me ev-er stray From Thee a-side.

No. 234. The Great Physician.

Wm. Hunter.   **J. H. Stockton.**

FINE.

1. { The great Phy-si-cian now is near, The sym-pa-thiz-ing Je-sus;
     He speaks the droop-ing heart to cheer, Oh! hear the voice of Je-sus. }
2. { Your man-y sins are all for-giv'n, Oh! hear the voice of Je-sus;
     Go on your way in peace to Heav'n, And wear a crown with Je-sus. }

D. S.—*Sweet-est car-ol ev-er sung,* Je-sus, bless-ed Je-sus.

REFRAIN.   D. S.

Sweetest note in ser-aph song, Sweet-est name on mor-tal tongue,

3 All glory to the dying Lamb!
  I now believe in Jesus;
  I love the blessed Savior's name,
  I love the name of Jesus.

4 His name dispels my guilt and fear,
  No other name but Jesus;
  Oh! how my soul delights to hear
  The charming name of Jesus.

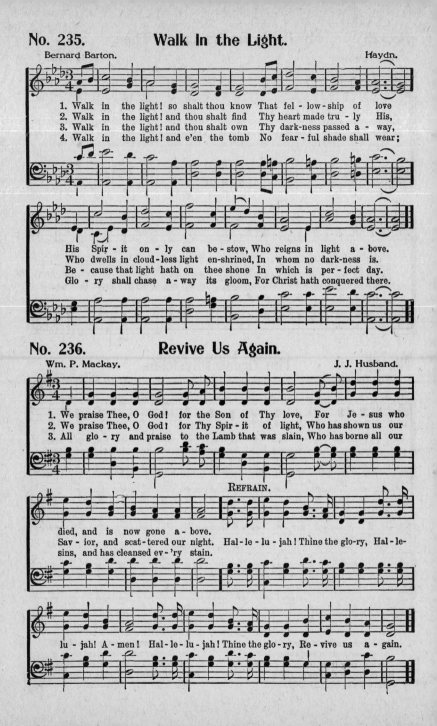

No. 235. Walk In the Light.

Bernard Barton.

Haydn.

1. Walk in the light! so shalt thou know That fel-low-ship of love
2. Walk in the light! and thou shalt find Thy heart made tru-ly His,
3. Walk in the light! and thou shalt own Thy dark-ness passed a-way,
4. Walk in the light! and e'en the tomb No fear-ful shade shall wear;

His Spir-it on-ly can be-stow, Who reigns in light a-bove.
Who dwells in cloud-less light en-shrined, In whom no dark-ness is.
Be-cause that light hath on thee shone In which is per-fect day.
Glo-ry shall chase a-way its gloom, For Christ hath conquered there.

No. 236. Revive Us Again.

Wm. P. Mackay.

J. J. Husband.

1. We praise Thee, O God! for the Son of Thy love, For Je-sus who
2. We praise Thee, O God! for Thy Spir-it of light, Who has shown us our
3. All glo-ry and praise to the Lamb that was slain, Who has borne all our

REFRAIN.

died, and is now gone a-bove.
Sav-ior, and scat-tered our night. Hal-le-lu-jah! Thine the glo-ry, Hal-le-
sins, and has cleansed ev-'ry stain.

lu-jah! A-men! Hal-le-lu-jah! Thine the glo-ry, Re-vive us a-gain.

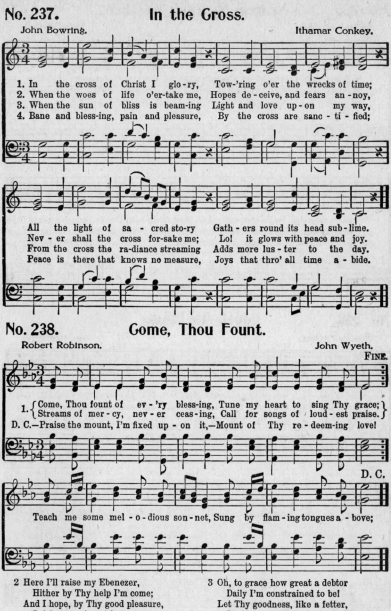

No. 237. In the Cross.

John Bowring. Ithamar Conkey.

1. In the cross of Christ I glo-ry, Tow-'ring o'er the wrecks of time;
2. When the woes of life o'er-take me, Hopes de-ceive, and fears an-noy,
3. When the sun of bliss is beam-ing Light and love up-on my way,
4. Bane and bless-ing, pain and pleasure, By the cross are sanc-ti-fied;

All the light of sa-cred sto-ry Gath-ers round its head sub-lime.
Nev-er shall the cross for-sake me; Lo! it glows with peace and joy.
From the cross the ra-diance streaming Adds more lus-ter to the day.
Peace is there that knows no measure, Joys that thro' all time a-bide.

No. 238. Come, Thou Fount.

Robert Robinson. John Wyeth.

FINE.

1. { Come, Thou fount of ev-'ry bless-ing, Tune my heart to sing Thy grace; }
   { Streams of mer-cy, nev-er ceas-ing, Call for songs of loud-est praise. }

D. C.—Praise the mount, I'm fixed up-on it,—Mount of Thy re-deem-ing love!

D. C.

Teach me some mel-o-dious son-net, Sung by flam-ing tongues a-bove;

2 Here I'll raise my Ebenezer,
  Hither by Thy help I'm come;
And I hope, by Thy good pleasure,
  Safely to arrive at home.
Jesus sought me when a stranger,
  Wandering from the fold of God;
He, to rescue me from danger,
  Interposed His precious blood.

3 Oh, to grace how great a debtor
  Daily I'm constrained to be!
Let Thy goodness, like a fetter,
  Bind my wand'ring heart to Thee.
Prone to wander, Lord, I feel it,
  Prone to leave the God I love;
Here's my heart, oh, take and seal it,
  Seal it for Thy courts above.

No. 239.   **Nearer, My God, to Thee.**

Sarah F. Adams.   Lowell Mason.

1. Near-er, my God, to Thee, Near-er to Thee! E'en tho' it be a cross That rais-eth me;
2. Tho' like a wan-der-er, The sun gone down, Darkness be o-ver me, My rest a stone;
3. There let the way appear Steps un-to heav'n; All that Thou sendest me, In mer-cy giv'n;

Still all my song shall be, Nearer, my God, to Thee, Nearer, my God, to Thee, Nearer to Thee!
Yet in my dreams I'd be Nearer, my God, to Thee, Nearer, my God, to Thee, Nearer to Thee!
An-gels to beck-on me Nearer, my God, to Thee, Nearer, my God, to Thee, Nearer to Thee!

No. 240.   **Just As I Am.**

Charlotte Elliott.   Wm. Bradbury.

1. Just as I am, with-out one plea, But that Thy blood was shed for me,
2. Just as I am, and wait-ing not To rid my soul of one dark blot,
3. Just as I am, tho' tossed a-bout With many a con-flict, many a doubt,

And that Thou bidd'st me come to Thee, O Lamb of God, I come! I come!
To Thee whose blood can cleanse each spot, O Lamb of God, I come! I come!
Fight-ing and fears with-in, with-out, O Lamb of God, I come! I come!

4 Just as I am—poor, wretched, blind;
Sight, riches, healing of the mind,
Yea, all I need in Thee to find,
O Lamb of God, I come! I come!

5 Just as I am—Thou wilt receive,
Wilt welcome, pardon, cleanse, relieve;
Because Thy promise I believe,
O Lamb of God, I come! I come!

No. 241. My Jesus, I Love Thee.

London Hymn Book.

A. J. Gordon.

1. { My Je - sus, I love Thee, I know Thou art mine; }
   { For Thee all the fol - lies of sin I re - sign; } My gra - cious Re-deem-

2. { I love Thee, be - cause Thou hast first lov - ed me, }
   { And purchased my par - don on Cal - va - ry's tree; } I love Thee for wear-

er, my Sav - ior art Thou; If ev - er I loved Thee, my Je - sus, 'tis now.

ing the thorns on Thy brow; If ev - er I loved Thee, my Je - sus, 'tis now.

3 In mansions of glory and endless delight,
I'll ever adore Thee in heaven so bright;
I'll sing with the glittering crown on my brow,
If ever I loved Thee, my Jesus, 'tis now.

No. 242. Holy Spirit, Faithful Guide.

M. M. W.

M. M. Wells.

FINE.

1. { Ho - ly Spir - it, faith-ful Guide, Ev - er near the Christian's side, }
   { Gen-tly lead us by the hand, Pil-grims in a des - ert land. } Wear-y souls for-

D. C.—Whisp'ring softly, "Wand'rer, come, Follow me, I'll guide thee home."

2. { Ev - er pres-ent, tru - est Friend, Ev - er near Thine aid to lend, }
   { Leave us not to doubt and fear, Grop-ing on in darkness drear. } When the storms are

D. C.—Whisper soft-ly, "Wand'rer, come, Fol - low me, I'll guide thee home."

D. C.

e'er re-joice, While they hear that sweetest voice,

rag-ing sore, Hearts grow faint, and hopes give o'er,

3 When our days of toil shall cease,
Waiting still for sweet release,
Nothing left but heaven and prayer,
Wondering if our names are there;
Wading deep the dismal flood,
Pleading naught but Jesus' blood;
Whisper softly, "Wanderer, come,
Follow me, I'll guide thee home."

No. 243. Savior, Like a Shepherd Lead Us.

Dorothy A. Thrupp.   William B. Bradbury

1. { Sav - ior, like a shepherd lead us, Much we need Thy tend'rest care; } Blessed Je-sus,
   { In Thy pleasant pastures feed us, For our use Thy folds prepare: }

2. { We are Thine; do Thou befriend us, Be the Guardian of our way; } Blessed Je-sus,
   { Keep Thy flock, from sin defend us, Seek us when we go a - stray: }

Blessed Jesus, Thou hast bought us, Thine we are; Jesus, Thou hast bought us, Thine we are.
Blessed Jesus, Hear, oh, hear us when we pray; Jesus, Hear, oh, hear us when we pray.

3 Thou hast promised to receive us,
   Poor and sinful though we be;
Thou hast mercy to relieve us,
   Grace to cleanse, and power to free:
      Blessed Jesus,
   We will early turn to Thee.

4 Early let us seek Thy favor,
   Early let us do Thy will;
Blessed Lord and only Savior,
   With Thy love our bosoms fill:
      Blessed Jesus,
   Thou hast loved us, love us still.

No. 244. I Love Thy Kingdom, Lord.

Timothy Dwight.   Handel.

1. I love Thy king-dom, Lord, The house of Thine a - bode; The Church our blest Re-

2. I love Thy Church, O God! Her walls be-fore Thee stand, Dear as the ap - ple

deem-er saved With His own precious blood.
of Thine eye, And gra - ven on Thy hand.

3 For her my tears shall fall,
   For her my prayers ascend;
To her my cares and toils be given,
   Till toils and cares shall end.

4 Beyond my highest joy
   I prize her heavenly ways,
Her sweet communion, solemn vows,
   Her hymns of love and praise.

No. 245. O Love That Wilt Not Let Me Go.

George Matheson.

Albert L. Peace.

1. O Love that wilt not let me go, I rest my wear-y soul in Thee; I give Thee
2. O Light that foll'west all my way, I yield my flick'ring torch to Thee; My heart re-
3. O Joy that seekest me thro' pain, I can-not close my heart to Thee; I trace the
4. O Cross that lift-est up my head, I dare not ask to hide from Thee; I lay in

back the life I owe, That in Thine ocean depths its flow May rich-er, full-er be.
stores its borrowed ray, That in Thy sunshine's glow its day May brighter, fair-er be.
rain-bow thro' the rain, And feel the promise is not vain That morn shall tearless be.
dust life's glo-ry dead, And from the ground there blossoms red Life that shall endless be.

No. 246. Jesus, the Very Thought of Thee.

Edward Caswall.

John B. Dykes.

1. Je - sus, the ver - y thought of Thee With sweetness fills my breast;
2. No voice can sing, no heart can frame, Nor can the mem-'ry find
3. O Hope of ev-'ry con-trite heart! O Joy of all the meek!
4. But what to those who find? ah! this No tongue or pen can show;

But sweet-er far Thy face to see, And in Thy pres - ence rest.
A sweet-er sound than Thy blest name, O Sav - ior of man-kind!
To those who fall, how kind Thou art! How good to those who seek!
The love of Je - sus, what it is None but His loved ones know.

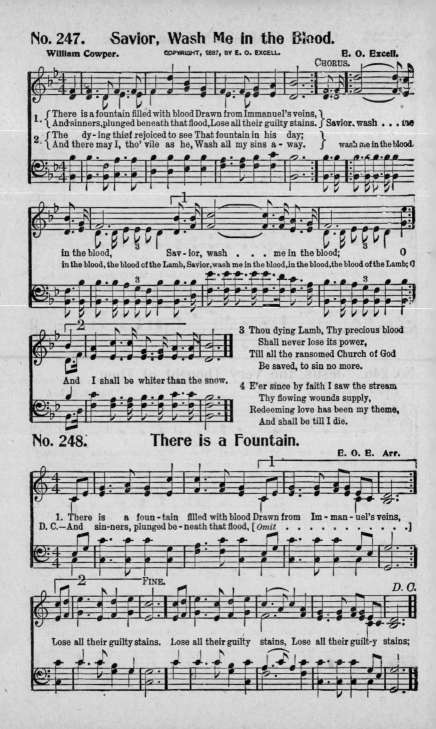

No. 247. Savior, Wash Me in the Blood.

William Cowper. COPYRIGHT, 1887, BY E. O. EXCELL. E. O. Excell.

CHORUS.

1. { There is a fountain filled with blood Drawn from Immanuel's veins,
   And sinners, plunged beneath that flood, Lose all their guilty stains. } Savior, wash . . . me

2. { The dy-ing thief rejoiced to see That fountain in his day;
   And there may I, tho' vile as he, Wash all my sins a-way. } wash me in the blood,

in the blood, Sav-ior, wash . . . me in the blood;

in the blood, the blood of the Lamb, Savior, wash me in the blood, in the blood, the blood of the Lamb; O

And I shall be whiter than the snow.

3 Thou dying Lamb, Thy precious blood
Shall never lose its power,
Till all the ransomed Church of God
Be saved, to sin no more.

4 E'er since by faith I saw the stream
Thy flowing wounds supply,
Redeeming love has been my theme,
And shall be till I die.

No. 248. There is a Fountain.

E. O. E. Arr.

1. There is a foun-tain filled with blood Drawn from Im-man-uel's veins,
D. C.—And sin-ners, plunged be-neath that flood, [Omit . . . .]

FINE.

Lose all their guilty stains. Lose all their guilty stains, Lose all their guilt-y stains;

D. C.

No. 249. All Hail the Power of Jesus' Name.

Edward Perronet.　　　　　　　　　　　　　　　　　　Oliver Holden.

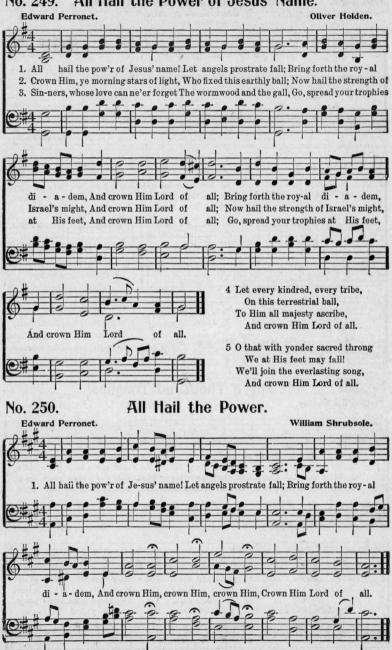

1. All　　hail the pow'r of Jesus' name! Let angels prostrate fall; Bring forth the roy - al
2. Crown Him, ye morning stars of light, Who fixed this earthly ball; Now hail the strength of
3. Sin-ners, whose love can ne'er forget The wormwood and the gall, Go, spread your trophies

di - a - dem, And crown Him Lord of　all; Bring forth the roy-al　di - a - dem,
Israel's might, And crown Him Lord of　all; Now hail the strength of Israel's might,
at　His feet, And crown Him Lord of　all;　Go, spread your trophies at　His feet,

And crown Him　Lord　　of　all.

4 Let every kindred, every tribe,
　On this terrestrial ball,
　To Him all majesty ascribe,
　And crown Him Lord of all.

5 O that with yonder sacred throng
　We at His feet may fall!
　We'll join the everlasting song,
　And crown Him Lord of all.

No. 250. All Hail the Power.

Edward Perronet.　　　　　　　　　　　　　　　　　　William Shrubsole.

1. All hail the pow'r of Je-sus' name! Let angels prostrate fall; Bring forth the roy - al

di - a - dem, And crown Him, crown Him, crown Him, Crown Him Lord of　all.

No. 251. Fade, Fade, Each Earthly Joy.

Mrs. Horatius Bonar.

JOHN R. CLEMENTS, OWNER.
USED BY PERMISSION.

T. E. Perkins.

1. Fade, fade, each earthly joy, Je-sus is mine! Break ev-'ry ten-der tie,
2. Tempt not my soul a-way, Je-sus is mine! Here would I ev-er stay,
3. Fare-well, ye dreams of night, Je-sus is mine! Lost in this dawn-ing light,

Je-sus is mine! Dark is the wil-der-ness, Earth has no rest-ing-place,
Je-sus is mine! Per-ish-ing things of clay, Born but for one brief day,
Je-sus is mine! All that my soul has tried Left but a dis-mal void,

Je-sus a-lone can bless, Je-sus is mine!
Pass from my heart a-way, Je-sus is mine!
Je-sus has sat-is-fied, Je-sus is mine!

4 Farewell, mortality,
    Jesus is mine!
Welcome, eternity,
    Jesus is mine!
Welcome, O loved and blest,
Welcome, sweet scenes of rest,
Welcome, my Savior's breast,
    Jesus is mine!

No. 252. Oh, For a Thousand Tongues.

Charles Wesley.

Carl Glasser

1. Oh, for a thou-sand tongues, to sing My great Re-deem-er's praise;
2. My gra-cious Mas-ter and my God, As-sist me to pro-claim,
3. Je-sus! the name that charms our fears, That bids our sor-rows cease;
4. He breaks the pow'r of can-celled sin, He sets the pris-'ner free;

The glo-ries of my God and King, The tri-umphs of His grace.
To spread thro' all the earth a-broad, The hon-ors of Thy name.
'Tis mu-sic in the sin-ner's ears, 'Tis life, and health, and peace.
His blood can make the foul-est clean; His blood a-vailed for me.

No. 253. From Greenland's Icy Mountains.

Reginald Heber.

Lowell Mason.

1. From Greenland's i - cy moun-tains, From In-dia's cor - al strand, Where Af-ric's
2. Shall we, whose souls are light - ed With wis-dom from on high, Shall we to
3. Waft, waft, ye winds, His sto - ry, And you, ye wa-ters, roll, Till, like a

sun - ny foun-tains Roll down their golden sand; From man - y an ancient riv - er, From
men be-night-ed The lamp of life de - ny? Sal - va - tion! O sal - va - tion! The
sea of glo - ry, It spreads from pole to pole: Till o'er our ransomed na-ture The

many a palm-y plain, They call us to de - liv - er Their land from error's chain.
joy - ful sound proclaim, Till earth's remotest na - tion Has learned Messiah's name.
Lamb for sinners slain, Re-deem-er, King, Cre-a - tor, In bliss re-turns to reign.

No. 254. Jesus Calls Us.

Cecil F. Alexander.

W. H. Jude.

1. Je - sus calls us: o'er the tu-mult Of our life's wild restless sea, Day by day His sweet voice
2. Jesus calls us from the worship Of the vain world's golden store; From each idol that would

sound-eth, Saying, "Christian, follow me."
keep us, Saying, "Christian, love me more."

3 In our joys and in our sorrows,
    Days of toil and hours of ease,
  Still He calls, in cares and pleasures,
    "That we love Him more than these."

4 Jesus calls us: by Thy mercies,
    Savior, make us hear Thy call;
  Give our hearts to Thine obedience,
    Serve and love Thee best of all.

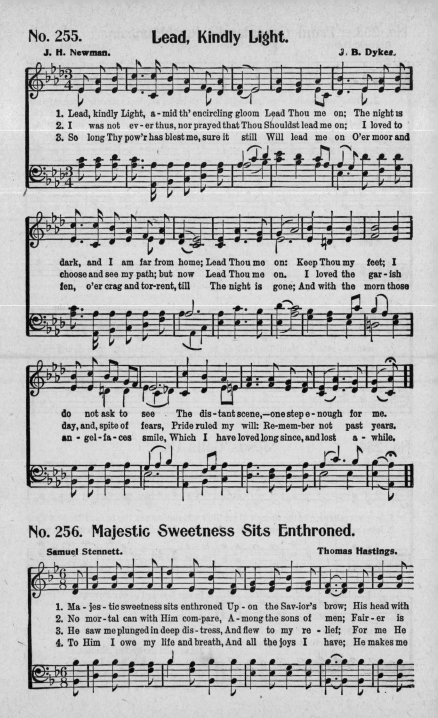

No. 255.

Lead, Kindly Light.

J. H. Newman.

J. B. Dykes.

1. Lead, kindly Light, a-mid th' encircling gloom Lead Thou me on; The night is
2. I was not ev-er thus, nor prayed that Thou Shouldst lead me on; I loved to
3. So long Thy pow'r has blest me, sure it still Will lead me on O'er moor and

dark, and I am far from home; Lead Thou me on: Keep Thou my feet; I
choose and see my path; but now Lead Thou me on. I loved the gar-ish
fen, o'er crag and tor-rent, till The night is gone; And with the morn those

do not ask to see The dis-tant scene,—one step e-nough for me.
day, and, spite of fears, Pride ruled my will: Re-mem-ber not past years.
an-gel-fa-ces smile, Which I have loved long since, and lost a-while.

No. 256. Majestic Sweetness Sits Enthroned.

Samuel Stennett.

Thomas Hastings.

1. Ma-jes-tic sweetness sits enthroned Up-on the Sav-ior's brow; His head with
2. No mor-tal can with Him com-pare, A-mong the sons of men; Fair-er is
3. He saw me plunged in deep dis-tress, And flew to my re-lief; For me He
4. To Him I owe my life and breath, And all the joys I have; He makes me

Majestic Sweetness Sits Enthroned.

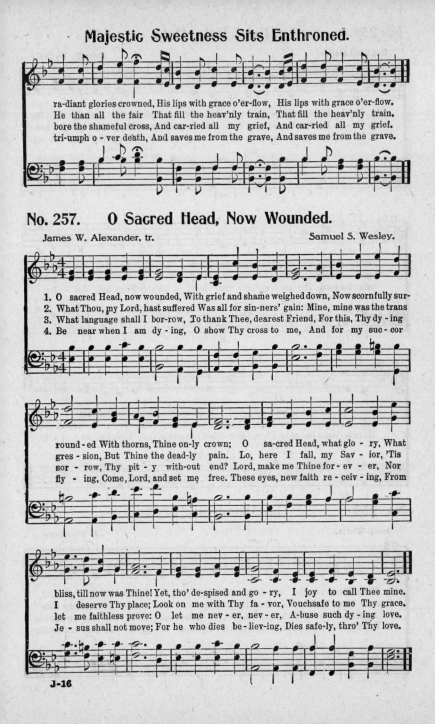

ra-diant glories crowned, His lips with grace o'er-flow, His lips with grace o'er-flow.
He than all the fair That fill the heav'nly train, That fill the heav'nly train.
bore the shameful cross, And car-ried all my grief, And car-ried all my grief.
tri-umph o-ver death, And saves me from the grave, And saves me from the grave.

No. 257.   O Sacred Head, Now Wounded.

James W. Alexander, tr.   Samuel S. Wesley.

1. O sacred Head, now wounded, With grief and shame weighed down, Now scornfully sur-
2. What Thou, my Lord, hast suffered Was all for sin-ners' gain: Mine, mine was the trans-
3. What language shall I bor-row, To thank Thee, dearest Friend, For this, Thy dy-ing
4. Be near when I am dy-ing, O show Thy cross to me, And for my suc-cor

round-ed With thorns, Thine on-ly crown; O sa-cred Head, what glo-ry, What
gres-sion, But Thine the dead-ly pain. Lo, here I fall, my Sav-ior, 'Tis
sor-row, Thy pit-y with-out end? Lord, make me Thine for-ev-er, Nor
fly-ing, Come, Lord, and set me free. These eyes, new faith re-ceiv-ing, From

bliss, till now was Thine! Yet, tho' de-spised and go-ry, I joy to call Thee mine.
I deserve Thy place; Look on me with Thy fa-vor, Vouchsafe to me Thy grace.
let me faithless prove: O let me nev-er, nev-er, A-buse such dy-ing love.
Je-sus shall not move; For he who dies be-liev-ing, Dies safe-ly, thro' Thy love.

Holy, Holy, Holy.

Reginald Heber.

John B. Dykes.

1. Ho - ly, ho - ly, ho - ly, Lord God Al - might - y! Ear - ly in the
2. Ho - ly, ho - ly, ho - ly! all the saints a - dore Thee, Cast - ing down their
3. Ho - ly, ho - ly, ho - ly! tho' the dark-ness hide Thee, Tho' the eye of

morn - ing our song shall rise to Thee: Ho - ly, ho - ly, ho - ly,
gold - en crowns a - round the glass - y sea; Cher - u - bim and sera - phim
sin - ful man Thy glo - ry may not see: On - ly Thou art ho - ly;

mer - ci - ful and might - y, God in Three Per - sons, bless-ed Trin - i - ty!
fall - ing down be - fore Thee, Which wert, and art, and ev - er-more shalt be.
there is none be - side Thee, Per - fect in pow'r, in love, and pu - ri - ty.

The Wondrous Cross.

Isaac Watts.

I. Woodbury.

1. When I sur - vey the won-drous cross On which the Prince of glo - ry died,
2. For - bid it, Lord, that I should boast, Save in the death of Christ, my God;
3. See, from His head, His hands, His feet, Sor - row and love flow min - gled down;
4. Were the whole realm of na - ture mine, That were a pres - ent far too small;

The Wondrous Cross.

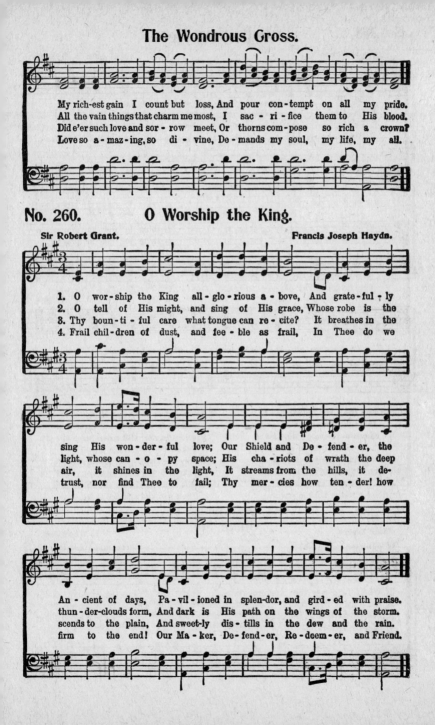

My rich-est gain I count but loss, And pour con-tempt on all my pride.
All the vain things that charm me most, I sac - ri - fice them to His blood.
Did e'er such love and sor - row meet, Or thorns com-pose so rich a crown?
Love so a - maz-ing, so di - vine, De - mands my soul, my life, my all.

No. 260.   O Worship the King.

Sir Robert Grant.   Francis Joseph Haydn.

1. O wor-ship the King all - glo - rious a - bove, And grate-ful - ly
2. O tell of His might, and sing of His grace, Whose robe is the
3. Thy boun-ti - ful care what tongue can re - cite? It breathes in the
4. Frail chil-dren of dust, and fee - ble as frail, In Thee do we

sing His won - der - ful love; Our Shield and De - fend - er, the
light, whose can - o - py space; His cha - riots of wrath the deep
air, it shines in the light, It streams from the hills, it de-
trust, nor find Thee to fail; Thy mer - cies how ten - der! how

An - cient of days, Pa - vil - ioned in splen-dor, and gird - ed with praise.
thun - der-clouds form, And dark is His path on the wings of the storm.
scends to the plain, And sweet-ly dis - tills in the dew and the rain.
firm to the end! Our Ma - ker, De - fend - er, Re - deem - er, and Friend.

No. 261. What a Friend.

H. Bonar.

C. C. Converse.

1. What a Friend we have in Je - sus, All our sins and griefs to bear!

What a priv - i - lege to car - ry Ev - 'ry-thing to God in prayer!

D. S.—All be-cause we do not car - ry Ev - 'ry-thing to God in prayer!

FINE.

O what peace we oft - en for - feit, O what need-less pain we bear,

D. S.

2 Have we trials and temptations?
  Is there trouble anywhere?
We should never be discouraged,
  Take it to the Lord in prayer.
Can we find a friend so faithful,
  Who will all our sorrows share?
Jesus knows our every weakness,
  Take it to the Lord in prayer.

3 Are we weak and heavy-laden,
  Cumbered with a load of care?—
Precious Savior, still our refuge,—
  Take it to the Lord in prayer.
Do thy friends despise, forsake thee?
  Take it to the Lord in prayer;
In His arms He'll take and shield thee,
  Thou wilt find a solace there.

No. 262. Guide Me.

W. Williams.

Thomas Hastings.

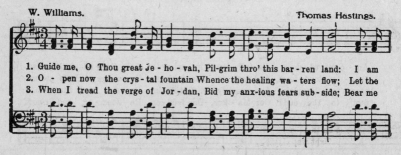

1. Guide me, O Thou great Je - ho - vah, Pil-grim thro' this bar - ren land: I am
2. O - pen now the crys - tal fountain Whence the healing wa - ters flow; Let the
3. When I tread the verge of Jor - dan, Bid my anx-ious fears sub - side; Bear me

Guide Me.

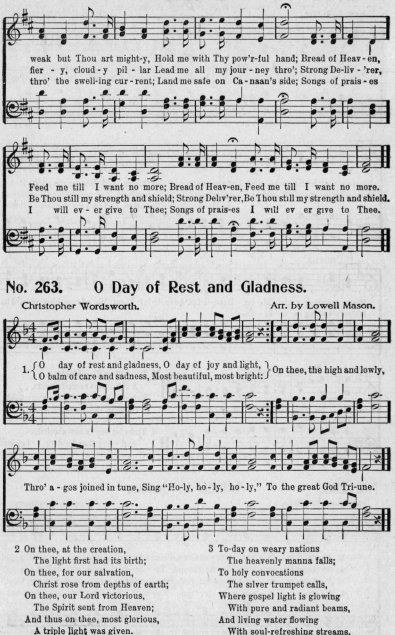

weak but Thou art might-y, Hold me with Thy pow'r-ful hand; Bread of Heav-en,
fier - y, cloud-y pil - lar Lead me all my jour-ney thro'; Strong De-liv - 'rer,
thro' the swell-ing cur-rent; Land me safe on Ca-naan's side; Songs of prais-es

Feed me till I want no more; Bread of Heav-en, Feed me till I want no more.
Be Thou still my strength and shield; Strong Deliv'rer, Be Thou still my strength and shield.
I will ev - er give to Thee; Songs of prais-es I will ev-er give to Thee.

No. 263.   O Day of Rest and Gladness.

Christopher Wordsworth.   Arr. by Lowell Mason.

1. { O   day of rest and gladness, O day of joy and light, } On thee, the high and lowly,
   { O balm of care and sadness, Most beautiful, most bright: }

Thro' a - ges joined in tune, Sing "Ho-ly, ho-ly, ho-ly," To the great God Tri-une.

2 On thee, at the creation,
  The light first had its birth;
On thee, for our salvation,
  Christ rose from depths of earth;
On thee, our Lord victorious,
  The Spirit sent from Heaven;
And thus on thee, most glorious,
  A triple light was given.

3 To-day on weary nations
  The heavenly manna falls;
To holy convocations
  The silver trumpet calls,
Where gospel light is glowing
  With pure and radiant beams,
And living water flowing
  With soul-refreshing streams.

No. 264. We're Marching to Zion.

COPYRIGHT PROPERTY OF MARY RUNYAN LOWRY.
USED BY PERMISSION.

Rev. I. Watts.   Rev. Robert Lowry.

1. Come, we that love the Lord, And let our joys be known; Join in a song with sweet accord,
2. Let those re - fuse to sing Who never knew our God; But children of the Heav'nly King,

Join in a song with sweet accord, And thus surround the throne, And thus surround the throne.
But children of the Heav'nly King May speak their joys abroad, May speak their joys abroad.
And thus surround the throne, And thus surround the throne.

CHORUS.

We're march-ing to Zi - on, Beau-ti-ful, beau-ti-ful Zi-on; We're marching upward to
We're marching on to Zi - on,

Zi - on, The beau-ti-ful Cit-y of God.
Zi-on, Zi-on,

3 The hill of Zion yields
   A thousand sacred sweets,
Before we reach the heav'nly fields,
   Or walk the golden streets.

4 Then let our songs abound,
   And ev'ry tear be dry;   [ground,
We're marching through Immanuel's
   To fairer worlds on high.

No. 265. Asleep in Jesus.

Margaret Mackay.   Wm. B. Bradbury.

1. A - sleep in Je - sus! bless - ed sleep, From which none ev - er wakes to weep!
2. A - sleep in Je - sus! O how sweet To be for such a slum - ber meet!
3. A - sleep in Je - sus! peace - ful rest, Whose waking is su - preme-ly blest!
4. A - sleep in Je - sus! O for me May such a bliss - ful ref - uge be!

Asleep in Jesus.

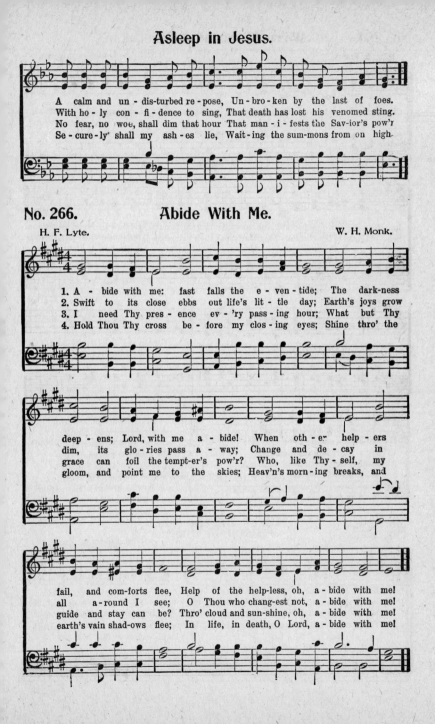

A calm and un-dis-turbed re-pose, Un-bro-ken by the last of foes.
With ho-ly con-fi-dence to sing, That death has lost his venomed sting.
No fear, no woe, shall dim that hour That man-i-fests the Sav-ior's pow'r
Se-cure-ly shall my ash-es lie, Wait-ing the sum-mons from on high.

No. 266. Abide With Me.

H. F. Lyte.

W. H. Monk.

1. A - bide with me: fast falls the e - ven - tide; The dark-ness
2. Swift to its close ebbs out life's lit - tle day; Earth's joys grow
3. I need Thy pres - ence ev - 'ry pass - ing hour; What but Thy
4. Hold Thou Thy cross be - fore my clos - ing eyes; Shine thro' the

deep - ens; Lord, with me a - bide! When oth - er help - ers
dim, its glo - ries pass a - way; Change and de - cay in
grace can foil the tempt-er's pow'r? Who, like Thy - self, my
gloom, and point me to the skies; Heav'n's morn - ing breaks, and

fail, and com-forts flee, Help of the help-less, oh, a - bide with me!
all a - round I see; O Thou who chang-est not, a - bide with me!
guide and stay can be? Thro' cloud and sun-shine, oh, a - bide with me!
earth's vain shad-ows flee; In life, in death, O Lord, a - bide with me!

No. 267. Jesus, I My Cross Have Taken.

Henry F. Lyte.

Mozart.

1. Je - sus, I my cross have ta - ken, All to leave, and fol - low Thee;

Na - ked, poor, de-spised, for - sa - ken, Thou from hence my all shalt be:

D. S.—Yet how rich is my con - di - tion, God and Heav'n are still my own!

Per - ish ev - 'ry fond am - bi - tion, All I've sought and hoped and known;

2 Let the world despise, forsake me,
They have left my Savior, too;
Human hearts and looks deceive me;
Thou art not, like man, untrue:
And, while Thou shalt smile upon me,
God of wisdom, love and might,
Foes may hate, and friends may shun me;
Show Thy face, and all is bright.

3 Go, then, earthly fame and treasure!
Come, disaster, scorn and pain!
In Thy service, pain is pleasure;
With Thy favor, loss is gain.
I have called Thee, "Abba, Father,"
I have stayed my heart on Thee;
Storms may howl, and clouds may gather,
All must work for good to me.

No. 268. Blest Be the Tie.

John Fawcett.

Hans George Naegeli.

1. Blest be the tie that binds Our hearts in Chris - tian love;
2. Be - fore our Fa - ther's throne, We pour our ar - dent prayers;
3. We share our mu - tual woes, Our mu - tual bur - dens bear;
4. When we a - sun - der part, It gives us in - ward pain;

Blest Be the Tie.

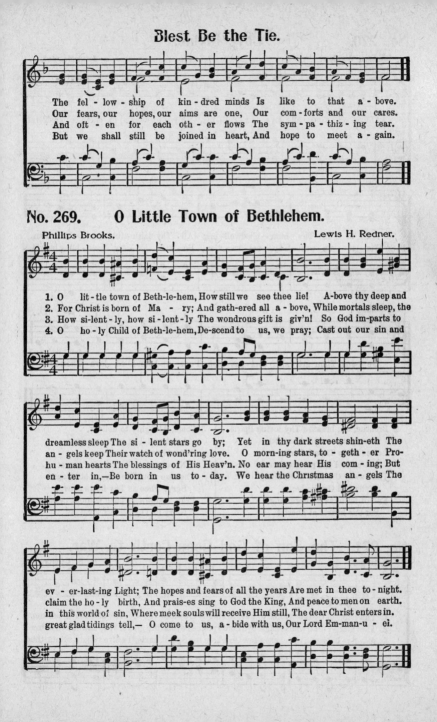

The fel - low - ship of kin - dred minds Is like to that a - bove.
Our fears, our hopes, our aims are one, Our com - forts and our cares.
And oft - en for each oth - er flows The sym - pa - thiz - ing tear.
But we shall still be joined in heart, And hope to meet a - gain.

No. 269.　O Little Town of Bethlehem.

Phillips Brooks.　　　　　　　　　　　　　　　Lewis H. Redner.

1. O lit - tle town of Beth-le-hem, How still we see thee lie! A-bove thy deep and
2. For Christ is born of Ma - ry; And gath-ered all a - bove, While mortals sleep, the
3. How si-lent-ly, how si-lent-ly The wondrous gift is giv'n! So God im-parts to
4. O ho - ly Child of Beth-le-hem, De-scend to us, we pray; Cast out our sin and

dreamless sleep The si - lent stars go by; Yet in thy dark streets shin-eth The
an - gels keep Their watch of wond'ring love. O morn-ing stars, to - geth - er Pro-
hu - man hearts The blessings of His Heav'n. No ear may hear His com - ing; But
en - ter in,—Be born in us to - day. We hear the Christmas an - gels The

ev - er-last-ing Light; The hopes and fears of all the years Are met in thee to - night.
claim the ho - ly birth, And prais-es sing to God the King, And peace to men on earth.
in this world of sin, Where meek souls will receive Him still, The dear Christ enters in.
great glad tidings tell,— O come to us, a - bide with us, Our Lord Em-man-u - el.

No. 270. Love Divine.

Charles Wesley.   John Zundel.

1. Love di - vine, all love ex - cell - ing, Joy of heav'n, to earth come down!

Fix in us Thy hum - ble dwell - ing; All Thy faith - ful mer - cies crown.
D. S.—Vis - it us with Thy sal - va - tion, En - ter ev - 'ry trem - bling heart!

Je - sus, Thou art all com - pas - sion, Pure, un - bound - ed love Thou art;

2 Breathe, oh, breathe Thy loving Spirit
    Into every troubled breast!
Let us all in Thee inherit,
    Let us find the promised rest.
Take away the love of sinning;
    Alpha and Omega be;
End of faith, as its beginning,
    Set our hearts at liberty!

3 Come, Almighty to deliver,
    Let us all Thy grace receive;
Suddenly return, and never,
    Never more Thy temples leave:
Thee we would be always blessing.
    Serve Thee as Thy hosts above,
Pray, and praise Thee without ceasing,
    Glory in Thy perfect love!

No. 271. The Son of God Goes Forth to War.

R. Heber.   H. S. Cutler.

1. The Son of God goes forth to war, A king - ly crown to gain; His blood - red ban - ner
2. That martyr first, whose eagle eye Could pierce beyond the grave; Who saw his Mas - ter
3. A no - ble band, the chosen few On whom the Spir - it came; Twelve valiant saints, their

The Son of God Goes Forth to War.

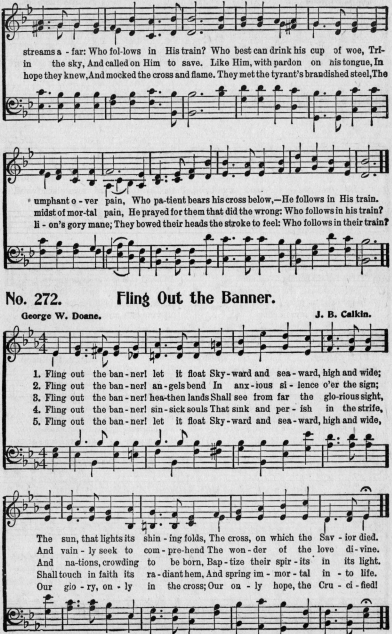

streams a - far: Who fol-lows in His train? Who best can drink his cup of woe, Tri-
in the sky, And called on Him to save. Like Him, with pardon on his tongue, In
hope they knew, And mocked the cross and flame. They met the tyrant's brandished steel, The

umphant o - ver pain, Who pa-tient bears his cross below,—He follows in His train.
midst of mor-tal pain, He prayed for them that did the wrong: Who follows in his train?
li - on's gory mane; They bowed their heads the stroke to feel: Who follows in their train?

No. 272. **Fling Out the Banner.**

George W. Doane.   J. B. Calkin.

1. Fling out the ban-ner! let it float Sky-ward and sea-ward, high and wide;
2. Fling out the ban-ner! an-gels bend In anx-ious si - lence o'er the sign;
3. Fling out the ban-ner! hea-then lands Shall see from far the glo-rious sight,
4. Fling out the ban-ner! sin-sick souls That sink and per - ish in the strife,
5. Fling out the ban-ner! let it float Sky-ward and sea-ward, high and wide,

The sun, that lights its shin-ing folds, The cross, on which the Sav - ior died.
And vain - ly seek to com-pre-hend The won - der of the love di - vine.
And na-tions, crowding to be born, Bap - tize their spir - its in its light.
Shall touch in faith its ra - diant hem, And spring im - mor - tal in - to life.
Our glo - ry, on - ly in the cross; Our on - ly hope, the Cru - ci - fied!

No. 273. Rock of Ages.

A. M. Toplady.

Thomas Hastings.

FINE.

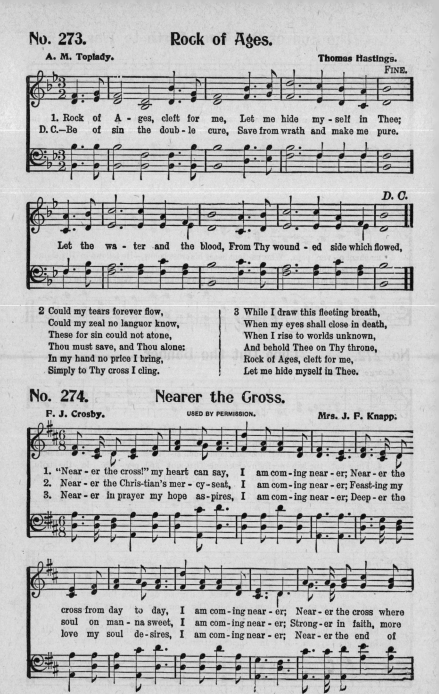

1. Rock of A - ges, cleft for me, Let me hide my - self in Thee;
D. C.—Be of sin the doub - le cure, Save from wrath and make me pure.

D. C.

Let the wa - ter and the blood, From Thy wound - ed side which flowed,

2 Could my tears forever flow,
　Could my zeal no languor know,
　These for sin could not atone,
　Thou must save, and Thou alone:
　In my hand no price I bring,
　Simply to Thy cross I cling.

3 While I draw this fleeting breath,
　When my eyes shall close in death,
　When I rise to worlds unknown,
　And behold Thee on Thy throne,
　Rock of Ages, cleft for me,
　Let me hide myself in Thee.

No. 274. Nearer the Cross.

F. J. Crosby.

USED BY PERMISSION.

Mrs. J. F. Knapp.

1. "Near - er the cross!" my heart can say, I am com - ing near - er; Near - er the
2. Near - er the Chris - tian's mer - cy - seat, I am com - ing near - er; Feast - ing my
3. Near - er in prayer my hope as - pires, I am com - ing near - er; Deep - er the

cross from day to day, I am com - ing near - er; Near - er the cross where
soul on man - na sweet, I am com - ing near - er; Strong - er in faith, more
love my soul de - sires, I am com - ing near - er; Near - er the end of

Nearer the Cross.

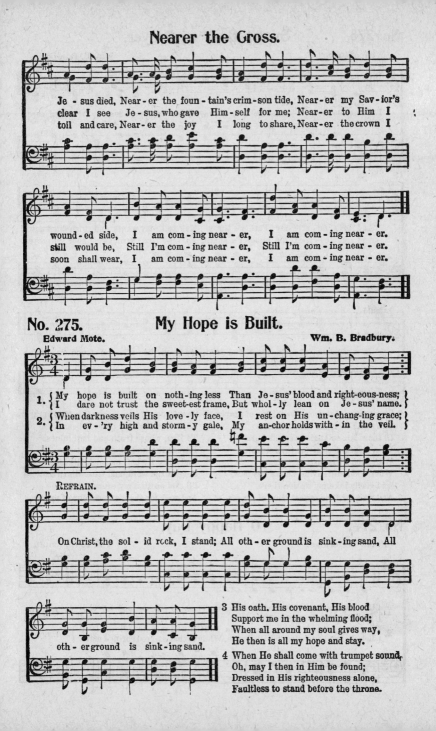

Je - sus died, Near - er the foun - tain's crim - son tide, Near - er my Sav - ior's
clear I see Je - sus, who gave Him - self for me; Near - er to Him I
toil and care, Near - er the joy I long to share, Near - er the crown I

wound - ed side, I am com - ing near - er, I am com - ing near - er.
still would be, Still I'm com - ing near - er, Still I'm com - ing near - er.
soon shall wear, I am com - ing near - er, I am com - ing near - er.

No. 275. My Hope is Built.

Edward Mote. Wm. B. Bradbury.

1. { My hope is built on noth - ing less Than Je - sus' blood and right-eous-ness; }
   { I dare not trust the sweet-est frame, But whol - ly lean on Je - sus' name. }

2. { When darkness veils His love - ly face, I rest on His un - chang-ing grace; }
   { In ev - 'ry high and storm - y gale, My an-chor holds with - in the veil. }

REFRAIN.

On Christ, the sol - id rock, I stand; All oth - er ground is sink - ing sand, All

oth - er ground is sink - ing sand.

3 His oath, His covenant, His blood
  Support me in the whelming flood;
  When all around my soul gives way,
  He then is all my hope and stay.

4 When He shall come with trumpet sound,
  Oh, may I then in Him be found;
  Dressed in His righteousness alone,
  Faultless to stand before the throne.

No. 276.   Sweet Hour of Prayer.

W. W. Walford.

Wm. B. Bradbury.

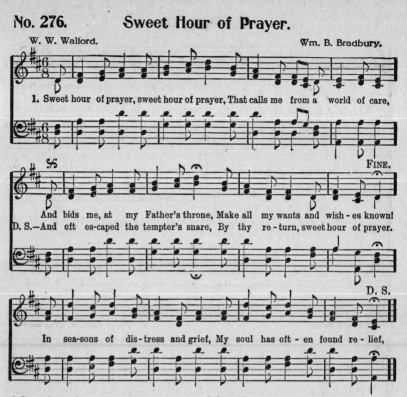

1. Sweet hour of prayer, sweet hour of prayer, That calls me from a world of care,

And bids me, at my Father's throne, Make all my wants and wish-es known!

D. S.—And oft es-caped the tempter's snare, By thy re-turn, sweet hour of prayer.

In sea-sons of dis-tress and grief, My soul has oft-en found re-lief,

2 Sweet hour of prayer, sweet hour of prayer,
The joys I feel, the bliss I share,
Of those whose anxious spirits burn
With strong desires for thy return!
With such I hasten to the place
Where God, my Savior, shows His face,
And gladly take my station there,
And wait for thee, sweet hour of prayer.

3 Sweet hour of prayer, sweet hour of prayer,
Thy wings shall my petition bear
To Him, whose truth and faithfulness
Engage the waiting soul to bless:
And since He bids me seek His face,
Believe His word, and trust His grace,
I'll cast on Him my every care,
And wait for thee, sweet hour of prayer.

No. 277.   O Happy Day.

Philip Doddridge.

E. F. Rimbault.

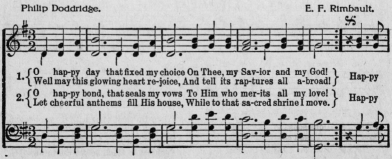

1. { O hap-py day that fixed my choice On Thee, my Sav-ior and my God!
Well may this glowing heart re-joice, And tell its rap-tures all a-broad! } Hap-py

2. { O hap-py bond, that seals my vows To Him who mer-its all my love!
Let cheerful anthems fill His house, While to that sa-cred shrine I move. } Hap-py

O Happy Day.

FINE.

day, hap-py day, When Je-sus washed my sins a-way. He taught me how to watch and

D. S.

pray, And live re-joic-ing ev'ry day;

3 'Tis done, the great transaction's done;
I am my Lord's, and He is mine;
He drew me, and I followed on,
Charmed to confess the voice divine.

4 Now rest, my long-divided heart,
Fixed on this blissful center, rest;
Nor ever from thy Lord depart,
With Him of every good possessed.

No. 278.   Sweet By-and-By.

S. Fillmore Bennett.

Jos. P. Webster.

1. {There's a land that is fair-er than day, And by faith we can see it a-far;
For the Fa-ther waits o-ver the way, To pre-[Omit................]

CHORUS.

pare us a dwelling-place there. In the sweet by-and-by, We shall meet on that

In the sweet by-and-by,

beau-ti-ful shore;   by-and-by.   We shall meet on that beautiful shore.

by-and-by;   by-and-by,

2 We shall sing on that beautiful shore
The melodious songs of the blest,
And our spirits shall sorrow no more,
Not a sigh for the blessing of rest.

3 To our bountiful Father above,
We will offer our tribute of praise,
For the glorious gift of His love,
And the blessings that hallow our days.

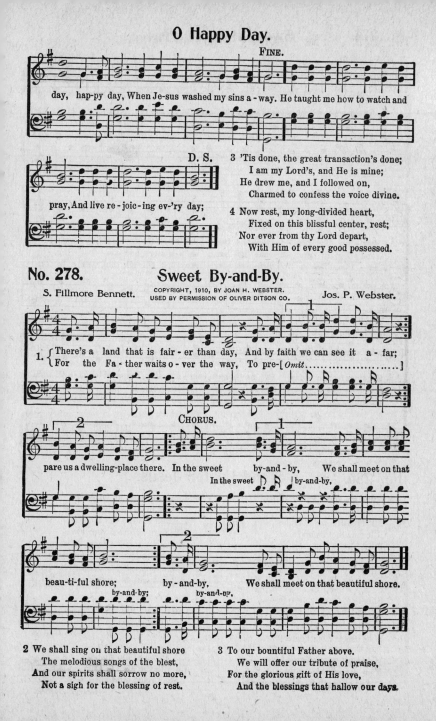

No. 279. The Morning Light is Breaking.

S. F. Smith.   G. J. Webb.

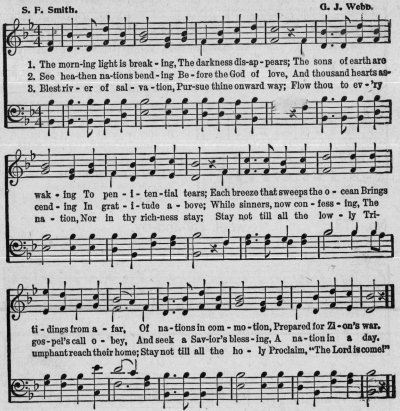

1. The morn-ing light is break-ing, The darkness dis-ap-pears; The sons of earth are wak-ing To pen-i-ten-tial tears; Each breeze that sweeps the o-cean Brings ti-dings from a-far, Of na-tions in com-mo-tion, Prepared for Zi-on's war.

2. See hea-then na-tions bend-ing Be-fore the God of love, And thousand hearts as-cend-ing In grat-i-tude a-bove; While sinners, now con-fess-ing, The gos-pel's call o-bey, And seek a Sav-ior's bless-ing, A na-tion in a day.

3. Blest riv-er of sal-va-tion, Pur-sue thine onward way; Flow thou to ev-'ry na-tion, Nor in thy rich-ness stay; Stay not till all the low-ly Tri-umphant reach their home; Stay not till all the ho-ly Proclaim, "The Lord is come!"

No. 280. Stand Up for Jesus.

1 Stand up, stand up for Jesus,
    Ye soldiers of the cross;
Lift high His royal banner,
    It must not suffer loss:
From victory unto victory
    His army shall He lead,
Till every foe is vanquished
    And Christ is Lord indeed.

2 Stand up, stand up for Jesus,
    The trumpet call obey;
Forth to the mighty conflict,
    In this His glorious day:
"Ye that are men, now serve Him,"
    Against unnumbered foes;
Your courage rise with danger,
    And strength to strength oppose.

3 Stand up, stand up for Jesus,
    Stand in His strength alone;
The arm of flesh will fail you;
    Ye dare not trust your own:
Put on the gospel armor,
    Each piece put on with prayer;
Where duty calls, or danger,
    Be never wanting there.

4 Stand up, stand up for Jesus,
    The strife will not be long;
This day the noise of battle,
    The next the victor's song:
To him that overcometh,
    A crown of life shall be;
He with the King of glory
    Shall reign eternally.

—*George Duffield*

RESPONSIVE READINGS

No. 281. PSALM 1.

1 Blessed is the man that walketh not in the counsel of the ungodly, nor standeth in the way of sinners, nor sitteth in the seat of the scornful. —

2 But his delight is in the law of the Lord; and in his law doth he meditate day and night.

3 And he shall be like a tree planted by the rivers of water, that bringeth forth his fruit in his season; his leaf also shall not wither, and whatsoever he doeth shall prosper.

4 The ungodly are not so; but are like the chaff which the wind driveth away.

5 Therefore the ungodly shall not stand in the judgment, nor sinners in the congregation of the righteous.

6 For the Lord knoweth the way of the righteous: but the way of the ungodly shall perish.

Hymn No. 235.

Walk in the Light.

No. 282. PSALM 5.

1 Give ear to my words, O Lord, consider my meditation.

2 Hearken unto the voice of my cry, my king and my God; for unto thee will I pray.

3 My voice shalt thou hear in the morning, O Lord; in the morning will I direct my prayer unto thee, and will look up.

4 For thou art not a God that hath pleasure in wickedness: neither shall evil dwell with thee.

5 The foolish shall not stand in thy sight: thou hatest all workers of iniquity.

6 Thou shalt destroy them that speak leasing: the Lord will abhor the bloody and deceitful man.

7 But as for me, I will come unto thy house in the multitude of thy mercy: and in thy fear will I worship toward thy holy temple.

8 Lead me, O Lord, in thy righteousness because of mine enemies; make thy way straight before my face.

Hymn No. 232.

Jesus, Savior, Pilot Me.

No. 283. PSALM 8.

1 O Lord, how excellent is thy name in all the earth! who hast set thy glory above the heavens.

2 Out of the mouths of babes and sucklings hast thou ordained strength, because of thine enemies, that thou mightest still the enemy and the avenger.

3 When I consider thy heavens, the work of thy fingers, the moon and the stars, which thou hast ordained;

4 What is man, that thou art mindful of him? and the son of man, that thou visitest him?

5 For thou hast made him a little lower than the angels, and hast crowned him with glory and honor.

6 Thou madest him to have dominion over the works of thy hands; thou hast put all things under his feet;

7 All sheep and oxen, yea, and the beasts of the field;

8 The fowl of the air, and the fish of the sea, and whatsoever passeth through the paths of the seas.

9 O Lord, our Lord, how excellent is thy name in all the earth!

Hymn No. 252.

Oh, for a Thousand Tongues, to Sing.

No. 284. PSALM 15.

1 Lord, who shall abide in thy tabernacle? who shall dwell in thy holy hill?

2 He that walketh uprightly, and worketh righteousness, and speaketh the truth in his heart.

3 He that backbiteth not with his tongue, nor doeth evil to his neighbor, nor taketh up a reproach against his neighbor.

4 In whose eyes a vile person is condemned; but he honoreth them that fear the Lord. He that sweareth to his own hurt, and changeth not.

5 He that putteth not out his money to usury, nor taketh reward against the innocent. He that doeth these things shall never be moved.

Hymn No. 241.

My Jesus, I Love Thee.

No. 285. PSALM 17.

1 Hear the right, O Lord, attend unto my cry; give ear unto my prayer, that goeth not out of feigned lips.

2 Let my sentence come forth from thy presence; let thine eyes behold the things that are equal.

3 Thou hast proved mine heart; thou hast visited me in the night; thou hast tried me, and shalt find nothing: I am purposed that my mouth shall not transgress.

4 Concerning the works of men, by the word of thy lips I have kept me from the paths of the destroyer.

5 Hold up my goings in thy paths, that my footsteps slip not.

6 I have called upon thee, for thou wilt hear me, O God: incline thine ear unto me, and hear my speech.

Hymn No. 262.

Guide me, O Thou Great Jehovah.

No. 286. PSALM 19.

1 The law of the Lord is perfect, converting the soul: the testimony of the Lord is sure, making wise the simple.

2 The statutes of the Lord are right, rejoicing the heart; the commandment of the Lord is pure, enlightening the eyes.

3 The fear of the Lord is clean, enduring forever: the judgments of the Lord are true and righteous altogether.

4 More to be desired are they than gold, yea, than much fine gold: sweeter also than honey and the honeycomb.

5 Moreover by them is thy servant warned; and in keeping of them there is great reward.

6 Who can understand his errors? cleanse thou me from secret faults.

7 Keep back thy servant also from presumptuous sins; let them not have dominion over me: then shall I be upright, and I shall be made innocent from the great transgression.

8 Let the words of my mouth, and the meditation of my heart, be acceptable in thy sight, O Lord, my strength, and my Redeemer.

Hymn No 230.

Break Thou the Bread of Life.

No. 287. PSALM 23.

1 The Lord is my Shepherd; I shall not want.

2 He maketh me to lie down in green pastures: he leadeth me beside the still waters.

3 He restoreth my soul: he leadeth me in the paths of righteousness for his name's sake.

4 Yea, though I walk through the valley of the shadow of death, I will fear no evil: for thou art with me; thy rod and thy staff they comfort me.

5 Thou preparest a table before me in the presence of mine enemies: thou anointest my head with oil; my cup runneth over

6 Surely goodness and mercy shall follow me all the days of my life: and I will dwell in the house of the Lord forever.

Hymn No. 254.

Jesus Calls Us.

No. 288. PSALM 24

1 The earth is the Lord's, and the fullness thereof; the world, and they that dwell therein.

2 For he hath founded it upon the seas, and established it upon the floods.

3 Who shall ascend into the the hill of the Lord? or who shall stand in his holy place?

4 He that hath clean hands, and a pure heart; who hath not lifted his soul unto vanity, nor sworn deceitfully.

5 He shall receive the blessing from the Lord, and righteousness from the God of his salvation.

6 This is the generation of them that seek him, that seek thy face, O Jacob. Selah.

7 Lift up your heads, O ye gates; and be ye lift up, ye everlasting doors; and the King of glory shall come in.

8 Who is this King of glory? The Lord strong and mighty, the Lord mighty in battle.

9 Lift up your heads, O ye gates; even lift them up, ye everlasting doors; and the King of glory shall come in.

10 Who is this king of glory? The Lord of hosts, he is the King of glory. Selah.

Hymn No. 260.

O Worship the King All-Glorious Above

Responsive Readings.

No. 289. PSALM 27.

1 The Lord is my light and my salvation; whom shall I fear? the Lord is the strength of my life; of whom shall I be afraid?

2 When the wicked, even mine enemies and my foes, came upon me to eat up my flesh, they stumbled and fell.

3 Though an host should encamp against me, my heart shall not fear: though war should rise against me, in this will I be confident.

4 One thing have I desired of the Lord, that will I seek after; that I may dwell in the house of the Lord all the days of my life, to behold the beauty of the Lord, and to enquire in his temple.

5 For in the time of trouble he shall hide me in his pavilion; in the secret of his tabernacle shall he hide me; he shall set me up upon a rock.

6 And now shall mine head be lifted up above mine enemies round about me; therefore will I offer in his tabernacle sacrifices of joy; I will sing, yea, I will sing praises unto the Lord.

7 Hear, O Lord, when I cry with my voice: have mercy also upon me, and answer me.

Sing No. 229.

Come, Thou Almighty King.

No. 290. PSALM 32.

1 Blessed is he whose transgression is forgiven, whose sin is covered.

2 Blessed is the man unto whom the Lord imputeth not iniquity, and in whose spirit there is no guile.

3 When I kept silence, my bones waxed old through my roaring all the day long.

4 For day and night thy hand was heavy upon me; my moisture is turned into the drought of summer. Selah.

5 I acknowledged my sin unto thee, and mine iniquity have I not hid. I said, I will confess my transgressions unto the Lord; and thou forgavest the iniquity of my sin. Selah.

6 For this shall every one that is godly pray unto thee in a time when thou mayest be found; surely in the floods of great waters they shall not come nigh unto him.

7 Thou art my hiding-place; thou shalt preserve me from trouble; thou shalt compass me about with songs of deliverance. Selah.

Sing No. 273.

Rock of Ages.

No. 291. PSALM 34.

1 I will bless the Lord at all times; his praise shall continually be in my mouth.

2 My soul shall make her boast in the Lord: the humble shall hear thereof, and be glad.

3 O magnify the Lord with me, and let us exalt his name together.

4 I sought the Lord, and he heard me, and delivered me from all my fears.

5 They looked unto him, and were lightened: and their faces were not ashamed.

6 This poor man cried, and the Lord heard him, and saved him out of all his troubles.

7 The angel of the Lord encampeth round about them that fear him, and delivereth them.

8 O taste and see that the Lord is good: blessed is the man that trusteth in him.

Sing No. 233.

My Faith Looks Up to Thee.

No. 292. PSALM 51.

1 Have mercy upon me, O God, according to thy loving-kindness: according unto the multitude of thy tender mercies blot out my transgressions.

2 Wash me thoroughly from mine iniquity, and cleanse me from my sin.

3 For I acknowledge my transgressions: and my sin is ever before me.

4 Against thee, thee only, have I sinned, and done this evil in thy sight: that thou mightest be justified when thou speakest, and be clear when thou judgest.

5 Behold, I was shapen in iniquity; and in sin did my mother conceive me.

6 Behold, thou desireth truth in the inward parts: and in the hidden part thou shalt make me to know wisdom.

7 Purge me with hyssop, and I shall be clean: wash me, and I shall be whiter than snow.

8 Make me to hear joy and gladness, that the bones which thou hast broken may rejoice.

9 Hide thy face from my sins, and blot out all my iniquities.

10 Create in me a clean heart, O God, and renew a right spirit within me.

Sing No. 275.

My Hope Is Built On Nothing Less.

No. 293. PSALM 61.

1 Hear my cry, O God; attend unto my prayer.

2 From the end of the earth will I cry unto thee, when my heart is overwhelmed; lead me to the rock that is higher than I.

3 For thou hast been a shelter for me, and a strong tower from the enemy.

4 I will abide in thy tabernacle forever: I will trust in the covert of thy wings. Selah.

5 For thou, O God, hast heard my vows; thou hast given me the heritage of them that fear thy name.

6 Thou wilt prolong the king's life: and his years as many generations.

7 He shall abide before God for ever; O prepare mercy and truth, which may preserve him.

8 So will I sing praise unto thy name for ever, that I may daily perform my vows.

Sing No. 236.

We Praise Thee, O God.

No. 294. PSALM 63.

1 O God, thou art my God; early will I seek thee; my soul thirsteth for thee, my flesh longeth for thee in a dry and thirsty land, where no water is;

2 To see thy power and thy glory, so as I have seen thee in the sanctuary.

3 Because thy loving-kindness is better than life, my lips shall praise thee.

4 Thus will I bless thee while I live; I will lift up my hands in thy name.

5 My soul shall be satisfied as with marrow and fatness; and my mouth shall praise thee with joyful lips:

6 When I remember thee upon my bed, and meditate on thee in the night watches.

7 Because thou hast been my help, therefore in the shadow of thy wings will I rejoice.

8 My soul followeth hard after thee: thy right hand upholdeth me.

9 But those that seek my soul, to destroy it, shall go into the lower parts of the earth.

10 They shall fall by the sword: they shall be a portion for foxes.

11 But the king shall rejoice in God; every one that sweareth by him shall glory: and the mouth of them that speak lies shall be stopped.

Sing No. 259.

When I Survey the Wondrous Cross.

No. 295. PSALM 65.

1 Praise waiteth for thee, O God, in Zion: and unto thee shall the vow be performed.

2 O thou that hearest prayer, unto thee shall all flesh come.

3 Iniquities prevail against me; as for our transgressions, thou shalt purge them away.

4 Blessed is the man whom thou choosest, and causest to approach unto thee, that he may dwell in thy courts: we shall be satisfied with the goodness of thy house, even thy holy temple.

5 By terrible things in righteousness wilt thou answer us, O God of our salvation; who art the confidence of all the ends of the earth, and of them that are afar off upon the sea:

6 Which by his strength setteth fast the mountains; being girded with power:

7 Which stilleth the noise of the seas, the noise of their waves, and the tumult of the people.

8 They also that dwell in the uttermost parts are afraid of thy tokens: thou makest the outgoings of the morning and evening rejoice.

9 Thou visitest the earth, and waterest it: thou greatly enrichest it with the river of God, which is full of water: thou preparest them corn, when thou hast so provided for it.

Sing No. 225.

Jesus, Lover of My Soul.

No. 296. PSALM 67.

1 God be merciful unto us, and bless us; and cause his face to shine upon us. Selah.

2 That thy way may be known upon earth, thy saving health among all nations.

3 Let the people praise thee, O God; let all the people praise thee.

4 O let the nations be glad and sing for joy: for thou shalt judge the people righteously, and govern the nations upon earth. Selah.

5 Let the people praise thee, O God; let all the people praise thee.

6 Then shall the earth yield her increase; and God, even our own God, shall bless us.

7 God shall bless us; and all the ends of the earth shall fear him.

Sing No. 110.

Count Your Blessings.

No. 297. PSALM 84.

1 How amiable are thy tabernacles, O Lord of hosts!

2 My soul longeth, yea, even fainteth for the courts of the Lord: my heart and my flesh crieth out for the living God.

3 Yea, the sparrow hath found an house, and the swallow a nest for herself, where she may lay her young, even thine altars, O Lord of hosts, my King, and my God.

4 Blessed are they that dwell in thy house: they will be still praising thee. Selah.

5 Blessed is the man whose strength is in thee; in whose heart are the ways of them.

6 Who passing through the valley of Baca make it a well: the rain also filleth the pools.

7 They go from strength to strength, every one of them in Zion appeareth before God.

8 O Lord God of hosts, hear my prayer: give ear, O God of Jacob. Selah.

9 Behold, O God, our shield, and look upon the face of thine anointed.

10 For a day in thy courts is better than a thousand. I had rather be a doorkeeper in the house of my God, that to dwell in the tents of wickedness.

11 For the Lord God is a sun and shield: the Lord will give grace and glory: no good thing will he withhold from them that walk uprightly.

12 O Lord of hosts, blessed is the man that trusteth in thee.

Sing No. 270.

Love Divine.

No. 298. PSALM 91.

1 He that dwelleth in the secret place of the Most High shall abide under the shadow of the Almighty.

2 I will say of the Lord, he is my refuge and my fortress: my God; in him will I trust.

3 Surely he shall deliver thee from the snare of the fowler, and from the noisome pestilence.

4 He shall cover thee with his feathers, and under his wings shalt thou trust: his truth shall be thy shield and buckler.

5 Thou shalt not be afraid for the terror by night; nor for the arrow that flieth by day;

6 Nor for the pestilence that walketh in darkness: nor for the destruction that wasteth at noonday.

7 A thousand shall fall at thy side, and ten thousand at thy right hand; but it shall not come nigh thee.

8 Only with thine eyes shalt thou behold and see the reward of the wicked.

9 Because thou hast made the Lord, which is my refuge, even the Most High, thy habitation.

Sing No. 239.

Nearer, My God, to Thee.

No. 299. PSALM 93.

1 The Lord reigneth, he is clothed with majesty: the Lord is clothed with strength, wherewith he hath girded himself: the world also is established, that it cannot be moved.

2 Thy throne is established of old; thou art from everlasting.

3 The floods have lifted up, O Lord, the floods have lifted up their voice; the floods lift up their waves.

4 The Lord on high is mightier than the noise of many waters, yea, than the mighty waves of the sea.

5 Thy testimonies are very sure: holiness becometh thine house, O Lord, for ever.

Sing No. 258.

Holy, Holy, Holy.

No. 300. PSALM 95.

1 O come, let us sing unto the Lord; let us make a joyful noise to the Rock of our salvation.

2 Let us come before his presence with thanksgiving, and make a joyful noise unto him with psalms.

3 For the Lord is a great God, and a great King above all gods.

4 In his hand are the deep places of the earth: the strength of the hills is his also.

5 The sea is his, and he made it: and his hands formed the dry land.

6 O come, let us worship and bow down: let us kneel before the Lord, our Maker.

7 For he is our God; and we are the people of his pasture, and the sheep of his hand.

Sing No. 260.

O Worship the King.

No. 301. PSALM 98.

1 O sing unto the Lord a new song; for he hath done marvelous things: his right hand, and his holy arm, hath gottten him the victory.

2 The Lord hath made known his salvation: his righteousness hath he openly showed in the sight of the heathen.

3 He hath remembered his mercy and his truth toward the house of Israel: all the ends of the earth have seen the salvation of our God.

4 Make a joyful noise unto the Lord, all the earth: make a loud noise, and rejoice, and sing praise.

5 Sing unto the Lord with the harp; with the harp, and the voice of a psalm.

6 With trumpets and sound of cornet make a joyful noise before the Lord, the King.

7 Let the sea roar, and the fullness thereof; the world, and they that dwell therein.

8 Let the floods clap their hands: let the hills be joyful together

9 Before the Lord; for he cometh to judge the earth: with righteousness shall he judge the world, and the people with equity.

Sing No. 228.

Jesus Shall Reign.

No. 302. PSALM 103.

1 Bless the Lord, O my soul: and all that is within me, bless his holy name.

2 Bless the Lord, O my soul, and forget not all his benefits.

3 Who forgiveth all thine iniquities; who healeth all thy diseases;

4 Who redeemeth thy life from destruction; who crowneth thee with loving-kindness and tender mercies;

5 Who satisfieth thy mouth with good things; so that thy youth is renewed like the eagle's.

6 The Lord executeth righteousness and judgment for all that are oppressed.

7 He made known his ways unto Moses, his acts unto the children of Israel.

8 The Lord is merciful and gracious, slow to anger, and plenteous in mercy.

9 He will not always chide: neither will he keep his anger forever.

10 He hath not dealt with us after our sins; nor rewarded us according to our iniquities.

11 For as the heaven is high above the earth, so great is his mercy toward them that fear him.

12 As far as the east is from the west, so far hath he removed our transgressions from us.

Sing No. 277.

O Happy Day.

No. 303. PSALM 119.

1 Blessed are the undefiled in the way, who walk in the law of the Lord.

2 Blessed are they that keep his testimonies, and that seek him with the whole heart.

3 They also do no iniquity: they walk in his ways.

4 Thou hast commanded us to keep thy precepts diligently.

5 O that my ways were directed to keep thy statutes!

6 Then shall I not be ashamed, when I have respect unto all thy commandments.

7 I will praise thee with uprightness of heart, when I shall have learned thy righteous judgments.

8 I will keep thy statutes: O forsake me not utterly.

Sing No. 153.

Where He Leads Me.

No. 304. PSALM 122.

1 I was glad when they said unto me, Let us go unto the house of the Lord.

2 Our feet shall stand within thy gates, O Jerusalem.

3 Jerusalem is builded as a city that is compact together.

4 Whither the tribes go up, the tribes of the Lord, unto the testimony of Israel, to give thanks unto the name of the Lord.

5 For there are set thrones of judgment, the thrones of the house of David.

6 Pray for the peace of Jerusalem: they shall prosper that love thee.

7 Peace be within thy walls, and prosperity within thy palaces.

8 For my brethren and companions sakes, I will now say, Peace be within thee.

9 Because of the house of the Lord our God I will seek thy good.

Sing No. 244.

I Love Thy Kingdom, Lord.

Responsive Readings.

1 I will praise thee with my whole heart; before the gods will I sing praise unto thee.

2 I will worship toward thy holy temple, and praise thy name for thy loving-kindness and for thy truth; for thou hast magnified thy word above all thy name.

3 In the day when I cried thou answeredst me, and strengthenedst me with strength in my soul.

4 All the kings of the earth shall praise thee, O Lord, when they hear the words of thy mouth.

5 Yea, they shall sing in the way of the Lord: for great is the glory of the Lord.

6 Though the Lord be high, yet hath he respect unto the lowly: but the proud he knoweth afar off.

7 Though I walk in the midst of trouble, thou wilt revive me: thou shalt stretch fort thine hand against the wrath of mine enemies, and thy right hand shall save me.

8 The Lord will perfect that which concerneth me: thy mercy, O Lord, endureth, for ever: forsake not the works of thine own hands.

Sing No. 256.

Majestic Sweetness.

No. 306. PSALM 142.

1 I cried unto the Lord with my voice; with my voice unto the Lord did I make my supplication.

2 I poured out my complaint before Him: I showed before Him my trouble.

3 When my spirit was overwhelmed within me, then thou knewest my path. In the way wherein I walked have they privily laid a snare for me.

4 I looked on my right hand, and beheld, but there was no man that would know me: refuge failed me; no man cared for my soul.

5 I cried unto thee, O Lord: I said, thou art my refuge and my portion in the land of the living.

6 Attend unto my cry: for I am brought very low; deliver me from my persecutors; for they are stronger than I.

7 Bring my soul out of prison, that I may praise thy name: the righteous shall compass me about, for thou shalt deal bountifully with me.

Sing No. 243.

Savior, Like a Shepherd Lead Us.

No. 307. PSALM 149.

1 Praise ye the Lord. Sing unto the Lord a new song, and his praise in the congregation of saints.

2 Let Israel rejoice in him that made him: let the children of Zion be joyful in their King.

3 Let them praise his name in the dance: let them sing praises unto him with the timbrel and harp.

4 For the Lord taketh pleasure in his people: he will beautify the meek with salvation.

5 Let the saints be joyful in glory: let them sing aloud upon their beds.

6 Let the high praises of God be in their mouth, and a two-edged sword in their hand;

7 To execute vengeance upon the heathen, and punishments upon the people.

8 To bind their kings with chains, and their nobles with fetters of iron;

9 To execute upon them the judgment written: this honor have all his saints. Praise ye the Lord.

Sing No. 229.

Come, Thou Almighty King.

No. 308. PSALM 150.

1 Praise ye the Lord. Praise God in his sanctuary: praise him in the firmament of his power.

2 Praise him for his mighty acts: praise him according to his excellent greatness.

3 Praise him with the sound of the trumpet: praise him with the psaltery and harp.

4 Praise him with the timbrel and dance: praise him with stringed instruments and organs.

5 Praise him upon the loud cymbals; praise him upon the high sounding cymbals.

6 Let everything that hath breath praise the Lord. Praise ye the Lord.

Sing No. 249.

All Hail the Power.

Responsive Readings.

No. 309. ISAIAH 53.

1 Who hath believed our report? and to whom is the arm of the Lord revealed?

2 For he shall grow up before him as a tender plant, and as a root out of a dry ground; he hath no form nor comeliness; and when we shall see him, there is no beauty that we should desire him.

3 He is despised and rejected of men; a man of sorrows, and acquainted with grief: and we hid as it were our faces from him; he was despised, and we esteemed him not.

4 Surely he hath borne our griefs, and carried our sorrows: yet we did esteem him stricken, smitten of God, and afflicted.

5 But he was wounded for our transgressions, he was bruised for our iniquities: the chastisement of our peace was upon him; and with his stripes we are healed.

6 All we like sheep have gone astray; we have turned every one to his own way; and the Lord hath laid on him the iniquity of us all.

No. 310. JOHN 3 1-6; 14-18.

1 There was a man of the Pharisees, named Nicodemus, a ruler of the Jews:

2 The same came to Jesus by night, and said unto him, Rabbi, we know that thou art a teacher come from God; for no man can do these miracles that thou doest, except God be with him.

3 Jesus answered and said unto him, Verily, verily, I say unto thee, Except a man be born again, he cannot see the kingdom of God.

4 Nicodemus said unto him, How can a man be born when he is old? can he enter the second time into his mother's womb, and be born?

5 Jesus answered, Verily, verily, I say unto thee, Except a man be born of water and of the Spirit, he cannot enter into the kingdom of God.

6 That which is born of the flesh is flesh; and that which is born of the Spirit is spirit.

7 And as Moses lifted up the serpent in the wilderness; even so must the Son of man be lifted up:

8 That whosoever believeth in him should not perish, but have eternal life.

9 For God so loved the world, that he gave his only begotten Son, that whosoever believeth in him should not perish, but have everlasting life.

10 For God sent not his Son into the world to condemn the world; but that the world through him might be saved.

11 He that believeth on him is not condemned; but he that believeth not is condemned already; because he hath not believed in the name of the only begotten Son of God.

No. 311. ISAIAH 55.

1 Ho, every one that thirsteth, come ye to the waters, and he that hath no money; come ye, buy, and eat; yea, come, buy wine and milk without money and without price.

2 Wherefore do ye spend money for that which is not bread? and your labor for that which satisfieth not? hearken diligently unto me, and eat ye that which is good, and let your soul delight itself in fatness.

3 Incline your ear, and come unto me; hear, and your soul shall live; and I will make an everlasting covenant with you, even the sure mercies of David.

4 Behold, I have given him for a witness to the people, a leader and commander to the people.

5 Behold, thou shalt call a nation that thou knowest not, and nations that knew not thee shall run unto thee because of the Lord thy God, and for the Holy One of Israel; for he hath glorified thee.

6 Seek ye the Lord while he may be found, call ye upon him while he is near:

7 Let the wicked forsake his way, and the unrighteous man his thoughts; and let him return unto the Lord, and he will have mercy upon him; and to our God, for he will abundantly pardon.

No. 312. MATTHEW 11: 20-30.

1 Then began he to upbraid the cities wherein most of his mighty works were done, because they repented not:

2 Woe unto thee, Chorazin! woe unto thee, Bethsaida! for if the mighty works which were done in you had been done in Tyre and Sidon, they would have repented long ago in sackcloth and ashes.

3 But I say unto you, It shall be more tolerable for Tyre and Sidon at the day of judgment, than for you.

Responsive Readings.

4 And thou Capernaum, which art exalted unto heaven, shalt be brought down to hell; for if the mighty works, which have been done in thee, had been done in Sodom, it would have remained until this day.

5 But I say unto you, That it shall be more tolerable for the land of Sodom in the day of judgment, than for thee.

6 At that time Jesus answered and said, I thank thee, O Father, Lord of heaven and earth; because thou hast hid these things from the wise and prudent, and hast revealed them unto babes.

7 Even so, Father: for so it seemed good in thy sight.

8 All things are delivered unto me of my Father; and no man knoweth the Son, but the Father; neither knoweth any man the Father, save the Son, and he to whomsoever the Son will reveal him.

9 Come unto me, all ye that labor and are heavy laden, and I will give you rest.

10 Take my yoke upon you and learn of me; for I am meek and lowly in heart; and ye shall find rest unto your souls.

11 For my yoke is easy, and my burden is light.

No. 313. CHRISTMAS.

1 And there were in the same country shepherds abiding in the field,

2 Keeping watch over their flock by night.

3 And, lo, the angel of the Lord came upon them, and the glory of the Lord shone round about them:

4 And they were sore afraid.

5 And the angel said unto them, Fear not: for behold, I bring you good tidings of great joy, which shall be to all people.

6 For unto you is born this day in the city of David a Savior, which is Christ the Lord.

7 And suddenly there was with the angel a multitude of the heavenly host, praising God, and saying,

8 Glory to God in the highest, and on earth peace, good-will toward men.

9 Now lettest thou thy servant depart, Lord, according to thy word, in peace;

10 For mine eyes have seen thy salvation, which thou hast prepared before the face of all peoples;

11 A light for revelation to the Gentiles, and the glory of thy people Israel.

12 Now unto the King eternal, incorruptible, invisible, the only God, be honor and glory for ever and ever. Amen.

No. 314. TEMPERANCE.

1 Who hath woe? who hath sorrow? who hath contentions? who hath babbling? who hath wounds without cause? who hath redness of eyes?

2 They that tarry long at the wine: they that go to seek mixed wine.

3 Look not thou upon the wine when it is red, when it giveth his color in the the cup, when it moveth itself aright. At the last it biteth like a serpent and stingeth like an adder.

4 Be not drunk with wine. Be not among wine bibbers; among riotous eaters of flesh.

5 For the drunkard and the glutton shall come to poverty: and drowsiness shall clothe a man with rags.

6 Wine is a mocker, strong drink is raging; and whosoever is deceived thereby is not wise.

7 None of us liveth to himself, and no man dieth to himself.

8 Let us not judge one another anymore: but judge this rather, that no man put a stumbling-block or an occasion to fall in his brother's way.

9 The kingdom of God is not meat and drink; but righteousness, and peace, and joy in the Holy Ghost.

10 He that in these things serveth Christ is acceptable to God, and approved of men.

11 Let us therefore follow after the things which make for peace, and things wherewith one may edify another.

12 For meat destroy not the work of God. It is good neither to eat flesh, nor to drink wine, nor anything whereby thy brother stumbleth, or is offended, or is made weak.

Responsive Readings.

No. 315. PROV. 3.

1 My son, forget not my law; but let thine heart keep my commandments:

2 For length of days, and long life, and peace, shall they add to thee.

3 Let not mercy and truth forsake thee: bind them about thy neck; write them up-on the table of thine heart.

4 So shalt thou find favor and good understanding in the sight of God and men.

5 Trust in the Lord with all thine heart; and lean not unto thine own understanding.

6 In all thy way acknowledge him, and he shall direct thy paths.

7 Be not wise in thine own eyes: fear the Lord and depart from evil.

Sing No. 267.

Jesus, I My Cross Have Taken.

No. 316. MATT. 5.

1 And seeing the multitudes, he went up into a mountain: and when he was set, his disciples came unto him:

2 And he opened his mouth, and taught them, saying,

3 Blessed are the poor in spirit: for theirs is the kingdom of heaven.

4 Blessed are they that mourn: for they shall be comforted.

5 Blessed are the meek: for they shall inherit the earth.

6 Blessed are they which do hunger and thirst after righteousness: for they shall be filled.

7 Blessed are the merciful: for they shall obtain mercy.

8 Blessed are the pure in heart: for they shall see God.

9 Blessed are the peacemakers: for they shall be called the children of God.

10 Blessed are they which are persecuted for righteousness' sake: for theirs is the kingdom of heaven.

11 Blessed are ye, when men shall revile you, and persecute you, and shall say all manner of evil against you falsely, for my sake.

12 Rejoice, and be exceeding glad: for great is your reward in heaven: for so persecuted they the prophets which were before you.

Sing No. 150

Faith of Our Fathers.

No. 317. The Apostles' Creed.

I believe in God the Father Almighty, Maker of heaven and earth; and in Jesus Christ his only Son, our Lord: who was conceived by the Holy Ghost, born of the Virgin Mary, suffered under Pontius Pilate; was crucified, dead and buried; the third day he rose from the dead; he ascended into heaven, and sitteth on the right hand of God the Father Almighty; from thence he shall come to judge the quick and the dead.

I believe in the Holy Ghost; the Holy Catholic Church, the communion of saints; the forgiveness of sins; the resurrecton of the body, and the life everlasting. Amen.

Sing No. 338.

Gloria Patri. No. 2.

No. 318. 1 COR. 13.

1 Though I speak with the tongues of men and of angels, and have not charity, I am become as sounding brass or a tinkling cymbal.

2 And though I have the gift of prophecy and understand all mysteries, and all knowledge: and though I have all faith, so that I could remove mountains, and have not charity, I am nothing.

3 And though I bestow all my goods to feed the poor, and though I give my body to be burned, and have not charity, it profiteth me nothing.

4 Charity suffereth long, and is kind; charity envieth not; charity vaunteth not itself, is not puffed up,

5 Doth not behave itself unseemly, seeketh not her own, is not easily provoked, thinketh no evil;

6 Rejoice not in iniquity, but rejoiceth in the truth;

7 Beareth all things, believeth all things, hopeth all things, endureth all things.

8 Charity never faileth: but whether there be prophecies, they shall fail; whether there be tongues, they shall cease; whether there be knowledge, it shall vanish away.

9 For we know in part, and we prophesy in part.

10 But when that which is perfect is come, then that which is in part shall be done away.

Sing No. 221.

Onward, Christian Soldiers.

ORDER OF SERVICE. No. 1.

Prepared by Marion Lawrance, Chicago, Ill.

No. 319.   The Names of Jesus.

Supt.—Stand up and bless the Lord your God for ever and ever; and blessed be Thy glorious name.

All Rise, Sing.—Music No. 256.

How sweet the name of Jesus sounds
  In a believer's ear!
It soothes his sorrows, heals his wound
  And drives away his fear.

It makes the wounded spirit whole,
  And calms the troubled breast;
'Tis manna to the hungry soul,
  And to the weary, rest.

Dear name! the rock on which I build,
  My shield and hiding-place;
My never-failing treasure, filled
  With boundless stores of grace!

I would Thy boundless love proclaim
  With every fleeting breath;
So shall the music of Thy name
  Refresh my soul in death.

Supt.—By how many Names and Titles is Our Savior mentioned in the Bible?

School.—Over two hundred and fifty.

Supt.—What are some of the Names given to Him hundreds of years before He was born?

School.—For unto us a Child is born, unto us a Son is given; . . and His name shall be called Wonderful, Counsellor, Mighty God, Everlasting Father, Prince of Peace.

Supt.—God has highly exalted Him, and given Him a name which is above every name.

Minister.—He is the King of kings, and Lord of lords.

Officers.—Chiefest among ten thousand.

Senior Dept.—Son of the living God.

Young Men's Dept.—Lion of the Tribe of Judah.

Young Women's Dept.—The Bright and Morning Star.

Intermediate Dept.—The Light of the World.

Junior Dept.—The Good Shepherd.

Supt.—Which of all His names is the sweetest?

School.—JESUS.

Sing.—Music No. 233.

Sweetest note in seraph song,
Sweetest name on mortal tongue,
Sweetest carol ever sung,
  Jesus, Blessed Jesus.

Supt.—Why was He called Jesus?

School.—Thou shalt call His name JESUS; for it is He that shall save His people from their sins.

Minister.—And in none other is there salvation: for neither is there any other name under heaven, that is given among men, wherein we must be saved.

Supt.—He is the Captain of our Salvation.

Officers.—The Author and Finisher of our Faith.

Senior Dept.—The Head of the Church.

Young Men's Dept.—He is the Way, the Truth and the Life.

Young Women's Dept.—The Precious Corner Stone.

Intermediate Dept. — The Friend of Sinners.

Junior Dept.—The Man of Sorrows.

Supt.—But of all His names, which is the sweetest?

School.—JESUS.

Sing.—Music No. 233.

Sweetest note in seraph song,
Sweetest name on mortal tongue,
Sweetest carol ever sung,
  Jesus, blessed Jesus.

Prayer.

Supt.—Oh, magnify the Lord with me, and let us exalt His name together.

Sing.—Music No. 219 or 249.

All Hail the Power of Jesus' Name!

(Be Seated.)

No. 320.

1. Instrumental Music.

(*Go quietly to your places. As soon as the music stops, the doors will be closed.*)

2. Silence.

3. School Stands.

(*At signal of piano or organ, sing, without music, the first verse of "All Hail the Power of Jesus' Name."*)

4. Superintendent's Greeting.

Supt. — Good morning, teachers and scholars.

School.—Good morning, Mr. (*Supply the superintendent's name.*)

5. Responsive Service.

Supt.—O come, let us sing unto Jeñovah.

School.—Let us make a joyful noise to the Rock of our salvation.

Sing.—Music No. 86.

If His love is in the soul,
And we yield to His control,
Sweetest music will the lonely hours beguile;
We may drive the clouds away,
Cheer and bless the darkest day,
If we keep the heart singing all the while.

CHORUS.

Keep the heart singing all the while;
Make the world brighter with a smile;
Keep the song ringing! lonely hours we
may beguile,
If we keep the heart singing all the while.

Supt.—And seeing the multitudes, He went up into the mountain: and when He had sat down, His disciples came unto Him:

School.—And He opened His mouth and taught them, saying:

Assistant Supt.—Blessed are the poor in spirit:

School.—For theirs is the kingdom of heaven.

Sing.—Music No. 110.

When you look at others with their land
and gold,
Think that Christ has promised you His
wealth untold;
Count your many blessings, money can-
not buy
Your reward in heaven, nor your home on
high

CHO.—Count your blessings,
Name them one by one;
Count your blessings,
See what God hath done.
Count your blessings,
Name them one by one;
Count your many blessings,
See what God hath done.

Supt.—Blessed are they that mourn:

School.—For they shall be comforted.

Sing.—Music No. 261.

What a Friend we have in Jesus,
All our sins and griefs to bear!
What a privilege to carry
Everything to God in prayer!
Oh, what peace we often forfeit,
Oh, what needless pain we bear,
All because we do not carry,
Everything to God in prayer!

Supt.—What does Peter say concerning the preciousness of Jesus?

School.—"Unto you who believe He is precious." (1. Pet. 2: 7.)

Sing.—Music No. 47.

So precious is Jesus, my Savior my King,
His praise all the day long with rapture I
sing;
To Him in my weakness for strength I can
cling,
For He is so precious to me.

CHO.—For He is so precious to me,
For He is so precious to me;
'Tis heaven below
My Redeemer to know,
For He is so precious to me.

6. Show of Bibles.

7. Reading of Lesson.

8. Prayer.

9. Song.

10. Lesson Study.

11. Song.

12. Scripture Drill.

13. Reports.

14. Closing Word.

15. Closing Song.—See No. 110.

More Like the Master.

ORDER OF SERVICE. No. 3.

No. 321.

Instrumental Music.

Silent Prayer.

Supt.—What is the Golden Text of the Bible?

School.—For God so loved the world that He gave His only begotten Son, that whosoever believeth on Him should not perish, but have everlasting life.

Sing.—Music No. 270.

Love divine, all love excelling,
   Joy of heaven, to earth come down,
Fix in us Thy humble dwelling,
   All Thy faithful mercies crown.
Jesus, Thou art all compassion,
   Pure, unbounded love Thou art;
Visit us with Thy salvation,
   Enter every trembling heart.

Supt.—Behold what manner of love the Father hath bestowed upon us that we should be called the children of God.

School.—For God sent not the Son into the world to judge the world; but that the world should be saved through Him.

Supt.—Who shall separate us from the love of Christ?

Minister.—Shall tribulation?

Teachers.—Or anguish?

Boys.—Or persecution?

Girls.—Or famine?

All.—Or nakedness?

Ass't Supt.—Or peril?

Sec'y.—Or sword?

All.—Nay, in all these things we are more than conquerors through Him that loved us.

For I am persuaded that neither death, nor life, nor angels, nor principalities, nor powers, nor things present, nor things to come,

Nor height, nor depth, nor any other creature shall be able to separate us from the love of God, which is in Christ Jesus our Lord.

Sing.—Music No. 241.

I will love Thee in life, I will love Thee in death,
And praise Thee as long as Thou lendest me breath;
And say, when the death-dew lies cold on my brow,
If ever I loved Thee, my Jesus, 'tis now.

Prayer.—(*Followed by Lord's Prayer.*)

Announcements.

Song.

Lesson Reading.

Lesson Study.

Song.

Review.

Instrumental Prayer Hymn.

Benediction.

ORDER OF SERVICE. No. 4.

Prepared by P. H. Welshimer, Canton, Ohio.

No. 322.

1. Instrumental.—(*Selection.*)

2. Song by School.—Music No. 18.
    The Touch of His Hand.

3. Show of Bibles.

4. Responsive Reading.—(Ps. 19: 7-14.

Song.—Music No. 159.

    Holy Bible, Book Divine.

6. Prayer.—(*Followed by Lord's Prayer.*)

7. Reading of Lesson.

8. Lesson Study.

(*Instrumental selection while classes are retiring to rooms.*)

9. Reassembling of Classes.

(*Instrumental selection while reassembling.*)

10. Song.—Music No. 50.
    Growing Dearer.

11. Five Minute General Supplemental Work.

12. Announcing Names of Visitors Present.

13. Special Music.

14. Report of Secretary.

15. Announcements.

16. Song.—Music No. 221.
    Onward, Christian Soldiers.

17. Prayer and Benediction.

Responsive Reading.

NOTE.—Before the Leader reads, the Organist should play to the ✱ for a prelude. See music below.

Wisdom.

Leader:—Remember now thy Creator in the days of thy youth. Serve Him with gladness, and magnify His name forever.

Response:—What shall I render unto the Lord for all His benefits towards me? I will take the cup of salvation and call upon the name of the Lord.

Leader:—Give us, O Lord, the wisdom from above, which is first pure, then peaceable, gentle, easy to be entreated, full of mercy and good fruits, without partiality, and without hypocrisy.

Response:—Whence then cometh wisdom? and where is the place of understanding.

Leader:—Behold, the fear of the Lord, that is wisdom, and to depart from evil is understanding.

Response:—Happy is the man that findeth wisdom, and the man that getteth understanding.

Leader:—The merchandise of it is better than the merchandise of silver, and the gain thereof than fine gold.

Response:—She is more precious than rubies.

Leader:—And all things thou canst desire are not to be compared unto her.

Response:—Length of days is in her right hand: and in her left hand riches and honor.

Leader:—Her ways are ways of pleasantness, and all her paths are peace.

Response:—She is a tree of life to them that lay hold upon her; and happy is every one that retaineth her.

Leader:—And beside this, giving all diligence, add to your knowledge temperance.

Response:—And to temperance, patience.

Leader:—And to patience, godliness.

Response:—And to godliness, brotherly kindness.

Leader:—And to brotherly kindness, charity.

All sing:—(*Sing promptly without interludes.*)

No. 324. How Gentle God's Commands.

George Naegeli.

1. How gen - tle God's com-mands! How kind His pre - cepts are!
2. His good - ness stands ap - proved, Un - changed from day to day:

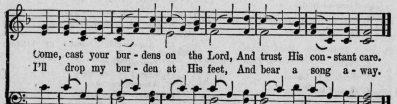

Come, cast your bur - dens on the Lord, And trust His con - stant care.
I'll drop my bur - den at His feet, And bear a song a - way.

PATRIOTIC AND TEMPERANCE

No. 325.
COPYRIGHT, 1902, BY E. O. EXCELL.
WORDS AND MUSIC.
Priscilla J. Owens.
Chas. Edw. Prior.

To the Rescue.

1. Death-bells toll-ing, toll-ing, toll-ing, Wrecks a-drift and breakers roll-ing;
2. Voi-ces cheering, life-boats steering, See, the help-ing hands are near-ing,
3. Joy-bells ring-ing, ring-ing, ring-ing, Friends a heart-y welcome bringing;

Where the floods of intemp'rance rave, Light the bea-con and speed to save.
While the pledge, our glad sig-nal, flies, Hope-ful mes-sage to wear-y eyes.
Heav'n bends down our joy a-near, Greets the res-cued with words of cheer.

Chorus.

Sign . . our pledge, now sign, And strength di-vine shall yet be thine;
Sign our pledge, oh, sign, now sign.

Sign . . . . our pledge, now sign, Touch not, taste not the wine.
Sign our pledge, oh, sign, now sign,

No. 326. Somebody's Boy.

Floy S. Armstrong.

Chas. H. Gabriel.

1. Homeless and friendless he wan-ders to-day In-to the pathways of shame;
2. Somewhere it may be a moth-er in prayer Whispers the wanderer's name;
3. See how the tempt-er, destructive and bold, Ev-er is seek-ing for prey;
4. Spurn then the gold from the dramseller's hand Buying your sanction to vice;

On-ly a drunkard, an outcast, you say, But he's somebody's boy, just the same.
Tho' he has spurned both her counsel and care He is some mother's boy, just the same.
Tales of wrecked manhood and ruin are told—Of the boys that are ruined each day.
Banish the dramshops that darken our land, For your boy and my boy pays the price.

CHORUS.

Some-bod-y's boy! some-bod-y's boy! What if that boy were mine?
He is Oh,

Some-bod-y's boy, some-bod-y's boy, What if that boy were thine?
He is

No. 327. Yield Not to Temptation.

H. R. P.   Dr. H. R. Palmer.

1. Yield not to temp-ta - tion, For yield-ing is sin; Each vic-t'ry will
2. Shun e - vil com-pan - ions, Bad language dis - dain; God's name hold in
3. To him that o'er-com-eth, God giv - eth a crown; Thro' faith we will

help you Some oth - er to win; Fight man-ful - ly on - ward,
rev - 'rence, Nor take it in vain; Be thought-ful and ear - nest,
con - quer, Tho' oft - en cast down; He who is our Sav - ior,

Dark passions sub - due; Look ev - er to Je - sus, He'll car-ry you thro'.
Kind-heart-ed and true; Look ev - er to Je - sus, He'll car-ry you thro'.
Our strength will re-new; Look ev - er to Je - sus, He'll car-ry you thro'.

CHORUS.

Ask the Sav - ior to help you, Com-fort, strengthen, and keep you;

He is will - ing to aid you, He will car - ry you thro'.

1-18

No. 328.   Touch Not, Taste Not.

USED BY PERMISSION.

Dwight Williams.   "Maryland."

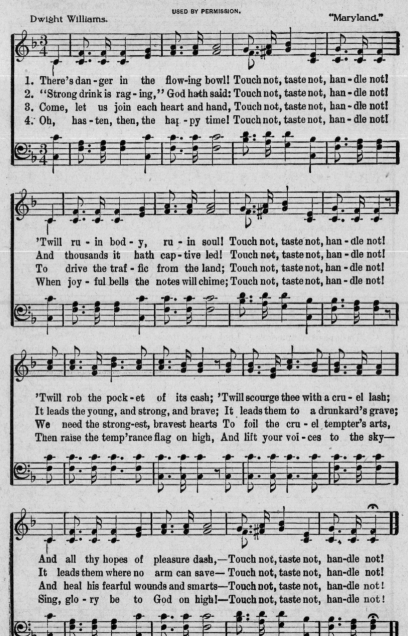

1. There's dan-ger in the flow-ing bowl! Touch not, taste not, han-dle not!
2. "Strong drink is rag-ing," God hath said: Touch not, taste not, han-dle not!
3. Come, let us join each heart and hand, Touch not, taste not, han-dle not!
4. Oh, has-ten, then, the hap-py time! Touch not, taste not, han-dle not!

'Twill ru-in bod-y, ru-in soul! Touch not, taste not, han-dle not!
And thousands it hath cap-tive led! Touch not, taste not, han-dle not!
To drive the traf-fic from the land; Touch not, taste not, han-dle not!
When joy-ful bells the notes will chime; Touch not, taste not, han-dle not!

'Twill rob the pock-et of its cash; 'Twill scourge thee with a cru-el lash;
It leads the young, and strong, and brave; It leads them to a drunkard's grave;
We need the strong-est, bravest hearts To foil the cru-el tempter's arts,
Then raise the temp'rance flag on high, And lift your voi-ces to the sky—

And all thy hopes of pleasure dash,—Touch not, taste not, han-dle not!
It leads them where no arm can save— Touch not, taste not, han-dle not!
And heal his fearful wounds and smarts—Touch not, taste not, han-dle not!
Sing, glo-ry be to God on high!—Touch not, taste not, han-dle not!

Was It You?

C. D. Martin.

Chas. H. Gabriel.

1. Some-bod-y vot-ed to ru-in my boy, Was that somebody you?
2. Some-bod-y ar-gued in fa-vor of wrong, Was that somebody you?
3. Some-bod-y turned all my day in-to night, Was that somebody you?
4. Some-bod-y li-censed an-oth-er to sell, Was that somebody you?

Some-bod-y helped his pure life to de-stroy, Was that some-bod-y you?
Some-bod-y hushed in my life a sweet song, Was that some-bod-y you?
Some-bod-y vot-ed to throt-tle the right, Was that some-bod-y you?
That which could turn Par-a-dise in-to hell, Was that some-bod-y you?

CHORUS.

Was that some-bod-y you?...... Was that some-bod-y you?......
was it you?   was it you?

Some-bod-y vot-ed to ru-in my boy, Was that somebody you?......
was it you?

No. 330.   The Temperance Army.

Charlotte G. Homer.

Mrs. Carrie B. Adams.

Cho.–1. March a-long to-geth-er, firm and true, For lo, the world is
2. On we go, with ar-mor shin-ing bright, With sword in hand to
3. True as steel, and loy-al to our King, We'll fight un-til the

ev-er watch-ing you; Be brave and bold up-on the bat-tle-field,
bat-tle for the right; U-nit-ed in the serv-ice of the Lord,
shouts of vic-t'ry ring From north to south, from east and from the west,

FINE.   UNISON SOLO.

De-ter-mined that the foe shall yield.   Loud and long the
We're marching at our Cap-tain's word.   Val-iant sol-diers
Till Christ is ev-'ry-where con-fessed.   Storm the forts of

bu-gle-call is sound-ing! Sin and wrong are ev-'ry-where a-bound-ing,
of the Lord are lead-ing; Ear-nest-ly for help the church is plead-ing;
sin and des-o-la-tion; Sol-diers brave, re-new your ob-li-ga-tion;

D. C. Cho.

"Forward!" all a-long the line resounding, Bids us march a-way.
Slow-ly backward see the foe re-ced-ing; Forward march to-day.
And with earnest prayer and sup-pli-ca-tion Forward march to-day.

The Red, White and Blue.

1. O Co-lum-bia! the gem of the o-cean,   The home of the brave and the free;
2. When war winged its wide des-o-la-tion,   And threatened the land to de-form,
3. Then, sons of Co-lum-bia, come hither,   And join in our nation's sweet hymn;

The   shrine of each patriot's de-vo-tion,   A   world offers homage to thee.
The   ark   then of freedom's foundation,   Co - lum-bia rode safe thro' the storm;
May the wreaths they have won never wither,   Nor the stars of their glory grow dim!

Thy   mandates make heroes assemble,   When Lib-er-ty's form stands in view;
With her garlands of vic-t'ry around her,   When so proudly she bore her brave crew,
May the serv-ice, u - nit-ed, ne'er sev-er,   But   they to their col-ors prove true!

Fine.

Thy   banners make tyr-an-ny tremble,   When borne by the red, white and blue.
With her flag proudly waving before her,   The boast of the red, white and blue.
The   Ar-my and Na-vy for-ev - er,   Three cheers for the red, white and blue.

Chorus.

D. S.

When borne by the red, white and blue,   When borne by the red, white and blue;
The   boast of the red, white and blue,   The   boast of the red, white and blue;
Three cheers for the red, white and blue,   Three cheers for the red, white and blue;

No. 332. Battle Hymn of the Republic.

Julia Ward Howe.   Melody, "Glory Hallelujah."

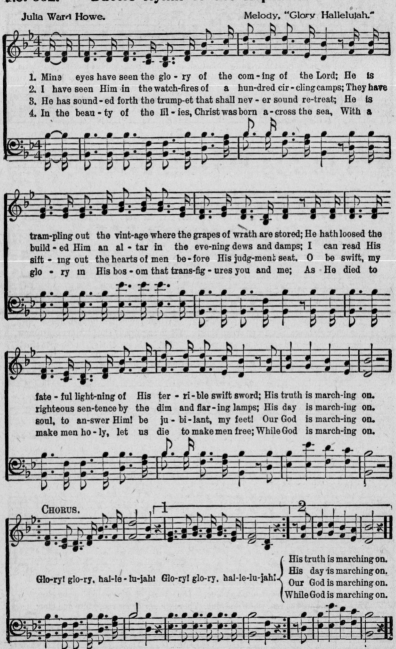

1. Mine eyes have seen the glo-ry of the com-ing of the Lord; He is
2. I have seen Him in the watch-fires of a hun-dred cir-cling camps; They have
3. He has sound-ed forth the trump-et that shall nev-er sound re-treat; He is
4. In the beau-ty of the lil-ies, Christ was born a-cross the sea, With a

tram-pling out the vint-age where the grapes of wrath are stored; He hath loosed the
build-ed Him an al-tar in the eve-ning dews and damps; I can read His
sift-ing out the hearts of men be-fore His judg-ment seat. O be swift, my
glo-ry in His bos-om that trans-fig-ures you and me; As He died to

fate-ful light-ning of His ter-ri-ble swift sword; His truth is march-ing on.
righteous sen-tence by the dim and flar-ing lamps; His day is march-ing on.
soul, to an-swer Him! be ju-bi-lant, my feet! Our God is march-ing on.
make men ho-ly, let us die to make men free; While God is march-ing on.

CHORUS.

Glo-ry! glo-ry, hal-le-lu-jah! Glo-ry! glo-ry, hal-le-lu-jah!
{ His truth is marching on.
  His day is marching on.
  Our God is marching on.
  While God is marching on.

No. 333. Fair Freedom's Land.

(THE WATCH ON THE RHINE.)

J. E. Rankin.

Carl Wilhelm.

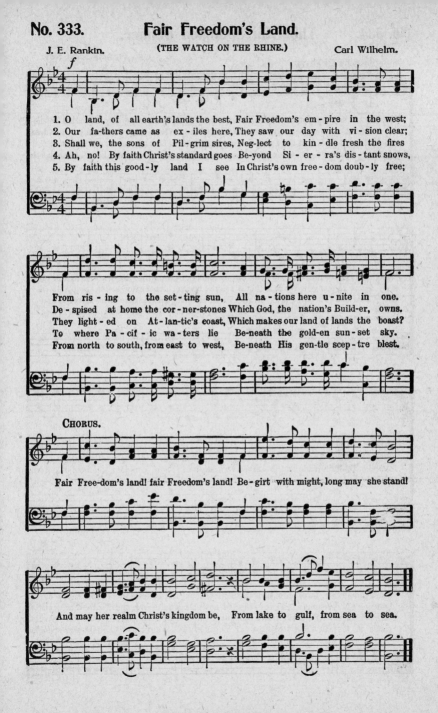

1. O land, of all earth's lands the best, Fair Freedom's em-pire in the west;
2. Our fa-thers came as ex-iles here, They saw our day with vi-sion clear;
3. Shall we, the sons of Pil-grim sires, Neg-lect to kin-dle fresh the fires
4. Ah, no! By faith Christ's standard goes Be-yond Si-er-ra's dis-tant snows,
5. By faith this good-ly land I see In Christ's own free-dom doub-ly free;

From ris-ing to the set-ting sun, All na-tions here u-nite in one.
De-spised at home the cor-ner-stones Which God, the nation's Build-er, owns.
They light-ed on At-lan-tic's coast, Which makes our land of lands the boast?
To where Pa-cif-ic wa-ters lie Be-neath the gold-en sun-set sky.
From north to south, from east to west, Be-neath His gen-tle scep-tre blest.

CHORUS.

Fair Free-dom's land! fair Freedom's land! Be-girt with might, long may she stand!

And may her realm Christ's kingdom be, From lake to gulf, from sea to sea.

No. 334. The Star-Spangled Banner.

Francis Scott Key.

SOLO OR QUARTET.

1. Oh, say, can you see by the dawn's early light, What so proudly we hailed at the
2. On the shore, dimly seen thro' the mists of the deep, Where the foe's haughty host in dread
3. And where is that band who so vauntingly swore, That the hav-oc of war and the
4. Oh, thus be it ev-er when freemen shall stand Between their loved homes and the

twilight's last gleaming? Whose broad stripes and bright stars, thro' the perilous fight, O'er the
si-lence re-pos-es, What is that which the breeze, o'er the tow-er-ing steep, As it
bat-tle's con-fu-sion, A home and a coun-try should leave us no more? Their
war's des-o-la-tion; Blest with vict'ry and peace, may the heav'n-rescued land Praise the

ramparts we watched, were so gal-lant-ly streaming? And the rockets' red glare, the bombs
fit ful-ly blows, half conceals, half dis-clos-es? Now it catch-es the gleam of the
blood has washed out their foul footsteps' pollution; No ref-uge could save the
Pow'r that hath made and preserved us a na-tion. Then con-quer we must, when our

CHORUS.

ff

burst-ing in air, Gave proof thro' the night that our flag was still there. Oh, say, does that
morning's first beam, In full glory reflected, now shines on the stream; 'Tis the star-spangled
hireling and slave From the terror of flight or the gloom of the grave. And the star-spangled
cause it is just, And this be our motto: "In God is our trust!" And the star-spangled

The Star-Spangled Banner.

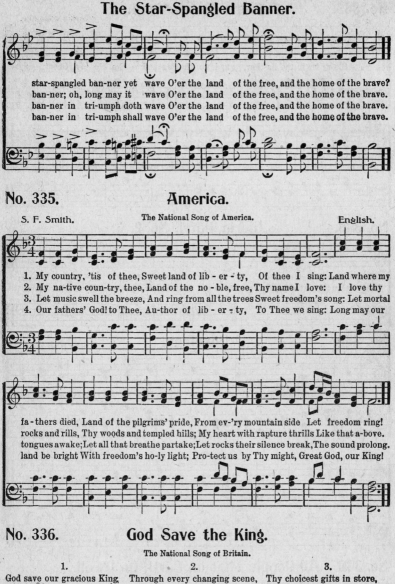

star-spangled ban-ner yet wave O'er the land of the free, and the home of the brave?
ban-ner; oh, long may it wave O'er the land of the free, and the home of the brave.
ban-ner in tri-umph doth wave O'er the land of the free, and the home of the brave.
ban-ner in tri-umph shall wave O'er the land of the free, and the home of the brave.

No. 335. America.

The National Song of America.

S. F. Smith.   English.

1. My country, 'tis of thee, Sweet land of lib-er-ty, Of thee I sing: Land where my
2. My na-tive coun-try, thee, Land of the no-ble, free, Thy name I love: I love thy
3. Let music swell the breeze, And ring from all the trees Sweet freedom's song: Let mortal
4. Our fathers' God! to Thee, Au-thor of lib-er-ty, To Thee we sing: Long may our

fa-thers died, Land of the pilgrims' pride, From ev-'ry mountain side Let freedom ring!
rocks and rills, Thy woods and templed hills; My heart with rapture thrills Like that a-bove.
tongues awake; Let all that breathe partake; Let rocks their silence break, The sound prolong.
land be bright With freedom's ho-ly light; Pro-tect us by Thy might, Great God, our King!

No. 336. God Save the King.

The National Song of Britain.

1.
God save our gracious King,
Long live our noble King,
God save the King:
Send him victorious,
Happy and glorious,
Long to reign over us;
God save the King.

2.
Through every changing scene,
O Lord, preserve our King;
Long may he reign:
His heart inspire and move
With wisdom from above,
And in a nation's love
His throne maintain.

3.
Thy choicest gifts in store,
On him be pleased to pour;
Long may he reign:
May he defend our laws,
And ever give us cause
To sing with heart and voice
God save the King.

No. 337. Gloria Patri, No. 1.

Charles Meineke.

Glo-ry be to the Fa-ther, and to the Son, and to the Ho-ly Ghost; As it was in the beginning, is now, and ever shall be, world without end, A-men, A-men.

No. 338. Gloria Patri, No. 2.

Gregorian.

Glory be to the Father, and to the Son, and to the Ho-ly Ghost;
As it was in the beginning, is now, and ev-er shall be, world with-out end. A-men.

No. 339. Doxology.

Louis Bourgeois.

Praise God, from whom all bless-ings flow; Praise Him, all crea-tures here be-low; Praise Him a-bove, ye heav'n-ly host; Praise Fa-ther, Son and Ho-ly Ghost.

No. 340. All People That on Earth Do Dwell.

Psalm 100.

1 All people that on earth do dwell,
  Sing to the Lord with cheerful voice;
  Him serve with mirth, His praise forth tell;
  Come ye before Him and rejoice.

2 Know that the Lord is God indeed;
  Without our aid He did us make;
  We are His flock, He doth us feed,
  And for His sheep He doth us take.

3 O enter then His gates with joy;
  Within His courts His praise proclaim;
  Let thankful songs your tongues employ;
  O bless and magnify His name.

4 Because the Lord our God is good,
  His mercy is forever sure;
  His truth at all times firmly stood,
  And shall from age to age endure.

GENERAL INDEX

(Alphabetical index arranged by first lines and titles)

A

A call for loyal soldiers.. 15
A LAMP WITHIN A STABLE 96
A land by faith I see....139
A LITTLE BIT OF LOVE.... 65
A little while and then.. 10
A sinner was wandering..207
A SONG OF VICTORY.......215
A vision goes before me.. 46
ABIDE WITH ME....... 266
Alas and did my Savior..154
ALL FOR JESUS 60
ALL HAIL IMMANUEL....213
ALL HAIL THE (DIADEM).219
ALL HAIL THE (CORO.)...249
ALL HAIL THE (M. LANE).250
All hail to thee 213
All of my need he freely 8
ALL PEOPLE THAT ON.....340
ALL THE WAY MY SAVIOR. 97
All things are ready..... 27
All yes all I give to Jesus 60
ALMOST PERSUADED ....:.145
ALONE WITH GOD........ 58
AMAZING GRACE 209
AMERICA 335
ANGRY WORDS O LET.....167
AS A VOLUNTEER 15
As I cling to the hand...200
ASLEEP IN JESUS 265
AT CALVARY 85
At calvary's cross 211
AT THE CROSS 154
Awake, awake 142, 210
AWAKENING CHORUS.....210

B

BATTLE HYMN OF THE....332
BE A HERO 163
Be not dismayed 37
BEAUTIFUL ISLE 107
BECAUSE HIS NAME IS ...193
BECAUSE I LOVE JESUS ... 49
Behold one cometh in....197
BETTER THAN I KNOW....190
BLEST BE THE TIE 268

BREAK THOU THE BREAD..230
Brightly beams our 147
BRING PEACE TO MY SOUL. 26
BRING THEM IN.........174
By sin's condemnation.. 85

C

Child of the Master..... 20
Christ found me lost....190
CHRIST SHALL BE KING... 70
Christ will me his aid.... 25
CLINGING CLOSE TO HIS...200
COME THOU ALMIGHTY...229
COME THOU FOUNT......238
COME TO THE FEAST..... 27
Come we that love the...264
COUNT YOUR BLESSINGS...110
Crown him, crown him...212
CROWN HIM KING OF....212
CROWN HIM WITH MANY. 11

D

DAY IS DYING IN THE.... 40
DEAR LITTLE STRANGER...172
DEATH BELLS ARE TOLLING.325
Does the world no rest.. 16
DON'T FORGET TO PRAY... 94
DOXOLOGY 339
Do you fear the foe.....166
Do you know the world.. 65
DRAW NIGH IMMANUEL..214
DRIVE IT AWAY WITH A.. 68

E

Earthly pleasures vainly. 21
ENTIRE CONSECRATION.... 24

F

FADE, FADE EACH 251
Failing in strength......194
FAIR FREEDOM'S LAND....333
FAITH OF OUR FATHERS...150
FAITH WILL BRING THE.. 76

FLING OUT THE BANNER..272
FOLLOW ME 124
FROM GREENLAND'S ICY...253
From over hill and plain. 55

G

Gird on your Steadfast..104
GIVE ME JESUS 149
GLORIA PATRI No. 1.....337
GLORIA PATRI No. 2.....338
Glory be to the 337-338
Glory to God for the.... 33
GOD IS CALLING YET...... 56
GOD SAVE THE KING.....336
GOD WILL TAKE CARE OF. 37
GOD'S PEACE 148
Go forth, go forth...... 80
Gone from my heart.....155
GRACE ENOUGH FOR ME... 23
GROWING DEARER EACH... 50
GROWING UP FOR JESUS..179
GUIDE ME 262

H

Had we only sunshine...165
Had you dwelt in.......198
HAPPY SONGLAND 186
Hark 'tis the shepherd's..174
Hark to the music 202
HARVEST SONG 126
HE IS ABLE TO DELIVER... 77
HE IS ALL IN ALL TO ME.106
HE IS KING 98
HE IS SO PRECIOUS TO ME. 44
HE KNOWS IT ALL 188
HE LOVES EVEN ME......187
HE LOVES EVERYBODY... 91
HE SUPPLIETH ALL OF MY. 8
HELP SOMEBODY TODAY... 35
High as the mountain... 72
High in the treetop's....170
His gifts are greater..... 19
HIS HOLY TEMPLE.......182
HIS LOVE FOR ME........196
HIS LOVE IS ALL I NEED.. 93

Holy Bible, book 159
Holy ghost with light.231
Holy, holy, holy.......258
Holy spirit faithful...242
Homeless and friendless.326
Honor bright cadets....171
How firm a 223-224
How gentle God's......324
How many times has he..122
How sweet is his love..206
How sweet is the love of 50

I

I am a stranger here.... 75
I am coming, lord......131
I am happy in him......192
I am so glad that our...184
I am thine, O Lord.... 29
I am thinking today 81
I can hear my Savior...153
I died broken-hearted..189
I dreamed one night....173
I have a song I love to.. 38
I hear thy welcome voice.131
I know my heavenly 195
I love him 155
I love thy kingdom.....244
I love to be alone with.. 58
I love to think my......188
I must needs go home... 71
I must tell Jesus 14
I saw one hanging on a.. 36
I stand all amazed 201
I think God gives the....164
I think when I read...181
I will not forget thee. 88
I would be like Jesus... 21
I would give my love... 99
I'll be a sunbeam.......160
I'll live for him.......144
I'm a pilgrim...........199
I've a message from the.117
I've found a friend....4-134
I've wandered far away..113
If Christ the Redeemer .. 43
If you are tired of the.. 59
If you need uplifting.... 76
If your heart keeps....112
In a world where 87
In his keeping......... 69
In his sunlight 74
In looking thro' my tears 23

In the cleft of the.... 72
In the cross 237
In the hour of trouble... 91
In the light and glory.... 74
In the shadow of his... 84
In vain I've tried 193
It came upon the......222
It is Jesus 197
It is well with my.... 12
It was his love........ 41

J

Jesus bids us shine.....176
Jesus, blessed Jesus ... 7
Jesus calls us 254
Jesus friend of sinners 3
Jesus I my cross have..267
Jesus is all the world.. 5
Jesus is calling 101
Jesus keep me near the..127
Jesus lover of my...225-226
Jesus loves me......178-185
Jesus loves even me....184
Jesus on the cross...... 46
Jesus saves 6
Jesus Savior pilot me..232
Jesus shall reign......228
Jesus the very.........246
Jesus wants me for a..160
Jesus was a child like.162
Jesus will 191
Jesus will sustain you. 16
Joy to the world....... 1
Just as I am..........240
Just the love of Jesus.. 48
Just when I need him.. 22

K

Keep the heart singing 86

L

Lamp of our feet 32
Land of the unsetting.. 52
Lay hold on the hope.... 53
Lead kindly light......255
Lead me Savior 123
Let him in 13
Let Jesus come into... 59
Let the lower lights..147
Let the sunshine in...166
Let those who've never..108

Let your light shine.... 57
Life wears a different.... 41
Like a chime of silver...124
Little sunbeams 164
Live in sunshine 45
Long by sin my eyes...106
Look all around you..... 35
Look and live 117
Look the harvest field...126
Lord I'm coming home..113
Lord make today 31
Lord take my all.......105
Love divine 270
Loudly unto the world...215
Low in a manger 172
Loyalty to Christ..... 55

M

Majestic sweetness 256
March along together...330
Mid the storms of doubt.216
Mine eyes have seen the.332
More about Jesus 119
More like the master..114
More love to thee.....133
My country 'tis of.....335
My days are gliding.....135
My faith looks up to..233
My father knows 195
My hope is built 275
My Jesus I love thee...241
My life I have given to.. 24
My life my love I give..144
My mother's song......208
My path may be lonely.. 49
My Savior first of all.118
My shepherd is the ...141
My soul is so happy.....192

N

Nearer my God to thee 239
Nearer still, nearer..: 125
Nearer the cross 274
Near the cross 127
No beautiful chamber..203
No dying there 139
No room in the inn....203
No time to pray 143
No tramp of marching.. 96
Nobody told me of.... 54
Nothing satisfies but.. 83
Now the day is over....151

O

O Columbia the gem of.331
O DAY OF REST AND......263
O GIFT DIVINE 66
O HAPPY DAY 277
O HOW I LOVE HIM......211
O how precious are the.. 34
O land of all Earth's....333
O LITTLE TOWN OF......269
O LOVE THAT WILT NOT..245
O SACRED HEAD NOW.....257
O sweet is the story of.. 92
O THAT WILL BE GLORY.. 73
O the unsearchable......103
O WHERE ARE THE......120
O WORSHIP THE KING....260
O ZION, HASTE 220
OH FOR A THOUSAND.....252
OH IT IS WONDERFUL....201
Oh say can you see.....334
Of the Savior and His 47
Once Jesus was a child..162
ONE DAY FOR THEE 31
One there is above all... 98
On the battlefield of life.163
ONWARD CHRISTIAN 221
ONWARD LITTLE SOLDIERS.177
OPEN THE DOOR FOR THE.161
Our Father which art in.180
OVER AND OVER AGAIN..122

P

PASS ME NOT 158
Praise God from whom..339

R

RAISE ME JESUS TO THY..204
REAPERS ARE NEEDED.202-218
REFUGE 225
RESCUE THE PERISHING.. 63
REVIVE US AGAIN 236
ROCK OF AGES 217-273
ROOM AT THE CROSS....137
ROSE, ROSE, ROSE.........168

S

SAFELY THROUGH 156
SAINTS IN GLORY 95
SATISFIED 82
SAVED, SAVED 134
SAVE ONE SOUL FOR...... 28
Savior lead me lest I....123

SAVIOR LIKE A SHEPHERD.243
SAVIOR MORE THAN LIFE..157
Savior thy dying love...129
SAVIOR WASH ME IN THE.247
SCATTER SUNSHINE 87
SERVANT OF GOD AWAKE.. 64
SERVING JESUS 183
SINCE I FOUND MY...... 42
SINCE I HAVE BEEN..... 38
Sing me the song my....208
Sing them over again to.121
Sinner why have you....146
SOMEBODY DID A GOLDEN..111
SOMEBODY KNOWS 194
SOMEBODY NEEDS YOU... 20
Somebody voted to ruin.329
SOMEBODY'S BOY 326
SOME DAY 136
Some day 't will all be...136
SOMEONE IS LOOKING.... 57
Some sweet day I shall.. 52
SOMETHING FOR JESUS...129
SOMETIME, SOMEWHERE ..205
SOMEWHERE BEYOND THE. 67
Somewhere the sun is...107
Song-land fair over.....186
So precious is Jesus.... 44
Sowing the seeds by the.140
SPEND ONE HOUR WITH.. 2
Standing in the market..218
STAND UP FOR JESUS.....280
STEPPING IN THE LIGHT.. 62
SUNSHINE AND RAIN.....165
SUN OF MY SOUL........227
Sweet are the promises.. 90
SWEET BY AND BY........278
SWEET HOUR OF PRAYER..276
Sweet is the promise.... 88
SWEETER THAN ALL...... 25

T

TAKE THE NAME OF...... 17
Take the world but give..149
TEACH ME 30
TELL IT WHEREVER YOU.. 43
TELL ME THE OLD, OLD..102
TELL THE STORY........ 47
THE BANNER OF THE....104
THE BIBLE 32
THE BIRDS' NEST 170
THE CHILDREN'S HOSANNA173
THE CHURCH IN THE.... 39

THE FIGHT IS ON.......132
THE GIFTS OF GOD 19
The glory song 73
THE GREAT PHYSICIAN...234
THE HALLELUJAH SONG...108
THE HOME OF ENDLESS... 79
THE HOPE SET BEFORE... 53
THE HOUR OF PRAYER... 33
THE KING'S BUSINESS.... 75
The Lord is in his holy..182
THE LORD'S PRAYER 180
The love of Jesus 93
THE MORNING LIGHT IS..279
THE OFFERING 105
THE OLD BOOK AND THE..216
THE RED, WHITE AND....331
THE SHINING SHORE.....135
THE SINNER AND THE...207
THE SON OF GOD GOES....271
THE STAR SPANGLED.....334
THE TEMPERANCE ARMY..330
THE TOUCH OF HIS HAND. 18
THE WAY OF THE CROSS.. 71
THE WONDERFUL STORY .. 92
THE WONDROUS CROSS....259
There are days so dark.. 18
THERE'S A FOUNTAIN.247-248
There's a church in the. 39
There's a land that is....278
There's a stranger at.... 13
There's danger in the....328
There's one who can.... 7
These little feet of mine.183
This world is not a place 45
Tho' burdens heavy..... 79
Tho' the way we journey 51
THY KINGDOM COME..... 89
Thy saints all stand..... 95
'TIS SO SWEET TO TRUST..109
'TIS SWEET TO KNOW.... 78
'TIS THE BLESSED HOUR.. 9
'TIS THE GRANDEST THEME 77
TO THE RESCUE 325
TO THE WORK 130
TOUCH NOT, TASTE NOT...328
Trying to walk in the.... 62
Try to save one soul.... 28

U

Unanswered yet 205
UNDER THE SNOW........175
UNSEARCHABLE RICHES...102

W

WALK IN THE LIGHT.....235
WAS IT YOU 329
Weary gleaner whence..116
Weary soul by sin...... 2
We bless thee for thy...148
We have heard the joyful 6
We may lighten toil and. 86
We praise thee O God..236
WE SHALL SEE THE KING. 51
WE'LL NEVER SAY FAIL...169
We're cadets that want..171
We're fighting for a.....169
WE'RE MARCHING TO ZION.264
WE'VE A STORY TO TELL... 61
WHAT A FRIEND 261
WHAT DID HE DO........115
What is making life so.. 48
What is sweeter, tell me.168

WHAT SHALL THE.......140
What tho' a cloud should 68
WHAT WONDROUS LOVE .. 36
WHAT WOULD YOU HAVE..198
When all my labors and. 73
When earthly cares and. 26
WHEN I GO HOME....... 10
When I have finished my 82
When I survey the......259
When I think of my....187
When my life-work is...118
When peace like a river. 12
When the day is dark... 94
When the early morning. 69
When troubled my soul.206
When upon life's billows.110
WHERE HAST THOU......116
Where he leads I'll..... 90
WHERE HE LEADS ME.....153

WHERE THOU CALLEST ME 34
While we pray and while.152
Who will open mercy's..191
WHY NOT COME TO HIM..146
WHY NOT NOW.........152
WHY STAND YE HERE....138
WILLING AM I.........128
WILL THERE BE ANY STARS 81
With sorrow and woe....189
WONDERFUL WORDS OF...121
WORKING, WATCHING.... 80
Would you care if some. 54

Y

YIELD NOT TO 327
You have heard of the...196
YOU MAY HAVE THE 100
You will live a life of....112

Order of Services

Order of Service No. 1 (The names of
    Jesus) 319
Order of Service No. 2.................320

Order of Service No. 3.................321
Order of Service No. 4.................322

Responsive Readings

And seeing the multitudes (Matt. 5)....316
And there were in the same country ...,313
Ho, every one that thirsteth (Isaiah 55).311
I believe in God (The Apostles' Creed)..317
My son, forget not (Prov. 3)..........315
Remember now thy Creator (Wisdom)..323

Then began He to upbraid (Matt. 11,
    20th to 30th verses)...............312
There was a man (John 3)...........310
Though I speak with the (1 Cor. 13)....318
Who hath believed (Isaiah 53).........309
Who hath woe (Temperance)..........314

Selected Psalms

I.   Blessed is the man.....281
V.   Give ear to my words....282
VIII.   O Lord, how excellent is.283
XV.   Lord, who shall abide...284
XVII.   Hear the right, O Lord..285
XIX.   The law of the Lord....286
XXIII.   The Lord is my shepherd.287
XXIV.   The earth is the Lord's..288
XXVII.   The Lord is my light....289
XXXII.   Blessed is he 290
XXXIV.   I will bless the Lord at..291
LI.   Have mercy upon me....292
LXI.   Hear my cry, O God....293
LXIII.   O God, Thou art my God.294

LXV.   Praise waiteth for thee..295
LXVII.   God be merciful unto us.296
LXXXIV.   How amiable are Thy...297
XCI.   He that dwelleth in the..298
XCIII.   The Lord reigneth......299
XCV.   O come let us sing unto.300
XCVIII.   O sing unto the Lord ...301
CIII.   Bless the Lord, O my....302
CXIX.   Blessed are the undefiled.303
CXXII.   I was glad when they....304
CXXXVIII.   I will praise Thee........305
CXXXII.   I cried unto the Lord....306
CXXXIX.   Praise ye the Lord......307
CL.   Praise ye the Lord......308

TOPICAL INDEX

Advent
(See Christmas)

Aspiration
Earthly pleasures..... 21
Glory to God........ 33
I am Thine........... 29
Jesus keep me.......127
More love to Thee....133
My life I have...... 24
Nearer my God.......239
Nearer the cross....274
Rock of Ages........273
Take the world......149

Assurance
All the way......... 97
All of my need...... 8
Be not dismayed..... 37
Christ will me...... 25
Does the world...... 16
High as the........ 72
I am Thine.......... 29
I have a song....... 38
I've found a friend..134
My hope is built....275
My Shepherd is 141
Sweet is the promise. 88
There's One who..... 7
'Tis the grandest... 77
'Tis so sweet.......109
When I have........ 82
When peace like..... 12
When the early..... 69

Atonement
Alas and did........154
A vision goes....... 46
By sin's condemnation 85
Gone from my.......155
I have a song....... 38
I hear Thy..........131
I've found a friend..134
In looking thro'.... 23
I saw one........... 36
Let those who've....108
Long by sin.........106
Lord take my all...105
My hope is built....275
My Jesus I love.....241
Nearer, still nearer.125
O happy day........277
Rock of Ages........273
Savior more than....157
There is a.......247-248
We praise Thee......236
When my life work...118
With sorrow and.....189

Bible
Break Thou the......230
Holy Bible, Book ...159
How firm a..........223
I've a message......117
Lamp of our feet... 32
Mid the storms......216
O the unsearchable..103
Sing them over......121

Children
Angry words........167
Growing up for Jesus.179
Had we only sunshine.165
Hark! tis the......174
High in the treetop's.170
I am so glad.......184
I dreamed one night..173
I think God gives...164
I think when I.....181
Jesus bids us shine.176
Jesus loves me ..178-185
Jesus wants me.....160
Low in the manger..172
March along........330
Once Jesus was.....162
On the battlefield..163
Open the door......161
Onward little......177
Our Father which...180
The Lord is in.....182
These little feet...183
Under the snow.....175
We're cadets that..171

We're fighting for...169
What is sweeter......168

Choruses
All hail the........219
All hail to Thee....213
As I cling..........200
At Calvary's cross..211
Awake! awake! 210
Awake! awake! the...142
Crown Him, crown...212
Draw nigh to us....214
Hark to the music..202
I'm a pilgrim......199
I stand all amazed..201
I've found a friend..134
Loudly unto the 215
'Mid the storms....216
Rock of Ages.......217
Standing in the....218
Songland fair......186
You have heard of..196

Christ
Christ shall be King. 70
Christ will me His.. 25
Crown him with..... 11
From over hill..... 55
High as the........ 72
Joy to the world... 1
Long by sin........106
More like the Master.114
More love to Thee..133
O Love that wilt...245
O the unsearchable..103
One there is above.. 98
There are days..... 18
We've a story...... 61

Christmas
All hail the....219-249
All hail to Thee....213
Crown Him, crown...212
Crown Him with..... 11
Draw nigh to us....214
Had you dwelt......198
It came upon.......222
Jesus shall reign..228
Joy to the world... 1
Low in a manger...172
No beautiful chamber.203
No tramp of marching 96
O little town......269

Citizenship
(See Patriotism)

Closing
Abide with me......266
All the way........ 97
Be not dismayed.... 37
Blest be the tie...268
Day is dying...... 40
Glory be to the...338
Guide me, Oh Thou..262
Holy spirit faithful.242
Jesus keep me near.127
Jesus Savior pilot me.232
Lead kindly Light..255
Now the day is.....151
Praise God from ...339
Savior lead me.....123
Savior like a 243
Sun of my soul.....227
Take the name of... 17
We bless Thee......148

Communion
(See Fellowship)

Conflict
A call for loyal... 15
Awake! awake! the..142
From over hill..... 55
Gird on your.......104
Go forth! Go forth. 80
On the battlefield..163
Onward, Christian ..221
Stand up for Jesus.280
Servant of God.... 64
The fight is on....132
The Son of God.....271
We're cadets that..171

Consecration
Ah, yes all, I give. 60

Come Thou Fount ...238
Earthly pleasures ... 21
I am thine 29
I can hear my.......153
I saw one 36
I've wandered far...113
I would give Thee .. 99
Jesus I my cross...267
Jesus is all 5
Jesus keep me near.127
Just as I am.......240
Lord, take my all..105
More like the......114
My life I have..... 24
My life, my love...114
Savior Thy dying..129
Teach me, O, Thou.. 30
Willing am I.......128

Cross
A vision goes...... 46
Fling out the banner.272
Gird on your.......104
I must needs go.... 71
I saw one hanging.. 36
In the cross.......237
Jesus keep me near.127
Nearer the cross...274
O Love that wilt...245
Room at the cross..137
When I survey......259

Devotion
(See Worship)

Duets
All, yes all, I give. 60
Christ found me lost.190
I love to think ...188
I stand all amazed..201
Long by sin my.....106
My soul is so 192
O gift divine..... 66
Raise me Jesus.....204
Some day 'twill ...136
Sowing the seed....140
There's One who.... 7
Unanswered yet.....205
Weary gleaner 116
Who will open......191
Why stand ye here .138
With sorrow and woe.189

Easter
All hail the....249-219
All hail to Thee ..213
At Calvary's cross..211
Awake! awake! and..210
Behold, one cometh..197
Christ shall be King. 70
Crown Him, crown..212
Crown Him with.... 11
Draw nigh to us....214
Had you dwelt......198
In the cross.......237
Jesus shall reign..228
Joy to the world... 1
Majestic sweetness.256
O Love that wilt...245
O sacred Head 259
One there is above.. 98
We've a story......61
With sorrow and woe.189

Evening Hymns
Abide with me......266
Be not dismayed.... 37
Day is dying...... 40
Glory to God...... 33
Jesus Savior, pilot.232
Lead kindly light..255
Nearer my God......239
Nearer still nearer.125
Now the day......151
O Love that wilt...245
Rock of Ages.......273
Savior lead me.....123
Savior like a 243
Sun of my soul.....227
Sweet hour of prayer.276
'Tis the blessed...9
Weary soul by 2
When the early.....69
When upon life's...110

Faith (See Trust)
Fellowship
Blest be the tie...268
I love to be alone.. 58
In the light...... 74
I've found a friend. 4
O how precious..... 34
Savior more than...157
There are days..... 18
'Tis the blessed... 9
Walk in the light..235
Weary soul by sin.. 2
What a friend......261

God
All of my need..... 8
Be not dismayed.... 37
God calling yet.... 56
His gifts are..... 19
Holy, Holy, Holy...258

Grace
Amazing grace......209
His Gifts are..... 19
How many times.....122
In looking thro'... 23
It was His love.... 41
O sweet is........ 92

Gratitude
How many times.....123
I love Thy.........244
O happy day........277
Safely thro'.......156
We bless Thee......148
When upon life's...110

Guidance
All the way........ 97
Does the world.... 16
Guide me..........262
I know my..........195
I must needs...... 71
Jesus, Friend of... 3
Jesus Savior pilot.232
Just when I need... 22
Lamp of our feet.. 32
Lead, kindly Light..255
Savior lead me.....123
Savior like a 243
Sweet are the..... 90
Sweet is the promise. 88
There are days..... 18
When the early.... 69

Heaven
A land by faith ...139
A little while 10
I am thinking 81
Let those who've...108
My days are........135
Some day 'twill ...136
Some sweet day.... 52
Somewhere beyond .. 67
Somewhere the sun .107
Songland fair......186
There's a land 278
Tho' burdens heavy. 79
Tho' the way...... 51
Thy saints all 95
When all my 73
When my lifework...118

Helpfulness
(See Service)
Holy Spirit
Holy Ghost 231
Holy Spirit, faithful.242
I love to be...... 58
O how precious.... 34
O Love that wilt...245
Teach me O Thou... 30
Walk in the light..235
We praise Thee.....236
When the early.... 39

Invitation
A call for loyal... 15
Alas and did my...154
All things are ready. 27
All yes all 66
Almost persuaded ..145
Brightly beams 147
By sin's condemnation 85

Does the world...... 16
Fade fade each.....251
God calling yet...... 56
Gone from my heart.155
I am a stranger..... 75
I am so glad......184
I can hear 153
I hear Thy 131
If you are tired 59
If you need 76
In the hour of...... 91
I've a message 117
I've found a Friend.134
I've wandered far...113
Jesus calls us 254
Jesus is tenderly ...101
Jesus keep me 127
Jesus, Lover of 225
Jesus Savior pilot ..232
Just as I am 240
Lay hold on........ 53
Like a chime 124
More like the......114
My hope is built ...275
My Jesus I love....241
Nearer the cross ...274
O happy day 277
O Love that wilt ...245
Pass me not 158
Rescue the perishing. 63
Rock of ages 273
Room at the cross...137
Sinner why have ...146
Take the name 17
The great Physician.234
There is a fountain247-248
There's a stranger... 13
'Tis the grandest ... 77
Try to save 28
We have heard 6
While we pray 152
Who will open 191

Jesus

A vision goes 46
All hail the power..249
All yes all I....... 60
Asleep in Jesus 265
Behold one cometh..197
Christ will me 25
Does the world 16
Fade, fade each....251
I must tell 14
If you are tired.... 59
In the hour of..... 91
I've found a Friend.. 4
Jesus calls us 254
Jesus Friend of.... 3
Jesus I my cross...267
Jesus is all 5
Jesus is tenderly ...101
Jesus Lover of 225
Jesus Savior pilot ..232
Jesus shall reign ...228
Jesus the very 246
Just when I need... 22
Love divine 270
Majestic sweetness .256
More about Jesus ..119
My Jesus I love ...241
My path may 49
Nothing satisfies .. 83
O sacred Head 257
O sweet is the..... 92
Oh for a thousand..252
Savior Thy dying..129
So precious is 44
Take the name 17
Tell me the old....102
The great Physician.234
The love of Jesus.. 93
There's One who ... 7
'Tis so sweet to....109
Weary soul by 2
What a Friend 261
What is making 48
Would you care.... 54

Love

At Calvary's cross..211
Christ found me ...190
Gone from my 155
How sweet is the .. 50
I stand all 201
In the hour 91
It was His love.... 41
Love divine all 270
My Jesus I love...241

My path may be 49
O gift divine 66
O Love that wilt ..245
Of the Savior 47
Tell me the 102
The love of 93
'Tis sweet to 78
What is making ... 48
When I think 187
When troubled 206
You have heard ...196

Memorial

A land by faith ...139
A little while 10
All the way my 97
Asleep in Jesus ...265
Be not dismayed .. 37
Does the world 16
Fade, fade. each...251
Jesus Lover of 225
Just when I need... 22
Lead, Kindly Light..255
Nearer my God 239
Rock of Ages 273
Some sweet day ... 52
Somewhere beyond . 67
Somewhere the sun .107
There's a land 278
There's One who ... 7
Tho' burdens heavy. 79
When earthly cares. 26

Missions

Awake! awake! 142
Brightly beams our..147
Child of the Master. 20
Christ shall be 70
Do you know 65
From Greenland's ..253
Go forth, Go forth. 80
Hark to the music..202
Jesus shall reign ..228
If Christ the 43
In a world where.. 87
Let your light 57
Look all around ... 35
Look, the harvest ..126
O where are the ..120
O Zion haste 229
Of the Savior 47
Servant of God ... 64
Standing in the.....218
The morning light..279
To the work 130
We have heard 6
Weary gleaner 116
We've a story 61
Why stand ye here.138
Would you care.... 54

Patriotism

God save our.......336
Mine eyes have seen..332
My country, 'tis 335
O Columbia the gem..331
O land of all 333
Oh say can you....334

Praise

All people that 340
Come Thou Almighty.229
Come Thou fount ..238
Come we that love..264
Crown Him with ... 11
Let those who've ..108
O worship the King.260
Oh for a thousand..252
So precious is Jesus. 44
We praise Thee ...236
When all my labors.. 73

Prayer

Glory to God 33
I love to be 58
I must tell Jesus... 14
No time to pray...143
Oh how precious .. 34
Oh listen to 115
Our Father which..180
Sweet hour of prayer.276
'Tis the blessed.... 9
Weary soul by sin.. 2
When earthly cares. 26
When the day...... 94

Sabbath

O day of rest.......263

Lord make today..... 31
Safely thro' 156

Sacrament

A vision goes....... 46
Break Thou the.....230
By sin's condemnation 85
Fade, fade each....251
I am thine 29
I can hear 153
I saw One 36
Jesus calls us 254
Jesus is all 5
Jesus, keep me.....127
Jesus Lover of 225
Jesus the very.....246
Just as I am.......240
Majestic sweetness .256
More love to Thee..133
My Jesus I love....241
Nearer my God.....239
Nearer still nearer ..125
Nearer the cross ...274
O how precious ... 34
O Love that wilt...245
O sacred Head 257
Savior more than ..157
Savior Thy dying..129
Take the world 149
The great Physician.234
'Tis so sweet......109
When earthly cares.. 26
When I survey.....259

Savior

How sweet is 50
In the light....... 74
I've found a 4
Life wears a 42
Pass me not 158
Savior lead me.....123
Savior like a 243
There's a Stranger.. 13
Trying to walk 62
When my life-work..118
You may have......100

Service

Child of the 20
Do you know 65
Go forth, Go forth. 80
In a world 87
Let your light 57
Look all around ... 35
Look the harvest...126
O where are the ..120
Rescue the perishing. 63
Savior Thy 129
Somebody did 111
To the work 130
Try to save 28
Weary gleaner 116
Why stand ye 138
Willing am I 128

Solos

A little while 10
A sinner was 207
Behold One cometh.197
Christ found me ...190
Do you know...... 65
Failing in strength..194
Had you dwelt.....198
Holy Bible, Book..159
I know my 195
I saw one 36
In vain I've tried...193
I've wandered far..113
Lord take my all..105
My soul is 192
No beautiful chamber.203
Sing me the song..208
Some sweet day.... 52
Somebody did 111
Somebody voted....329
Somewhere beyond . 67
Unanswered yet 205
What tho' a....... 68
When I think 187
When troubled 206
Who will open 191
You have heard....196

Sunshine Songs

Do you fear.......166
Had we only...... 165
I think God.......164
In a world 87
In the light........ 74

Jesus bids us 176
Jesus wants me 160
Let those who've ..168
Trying to walk 62
We may lighten.... 86
What tho' a 68
You will live.......112

Temperance

A call for loyal..... 15
Death bells tolling..325
From over hill..... 55
Gird on your......104
Homeless and friend-
  less 326
I am a stranger.... 75
In a world 87
Loudly unto the....215
March along 332
Mine eyes have ...332
On the battlefield ..163
Onward Christian ..221
Rescue the perishing. 63
Somebody voted....329
Sowing the seed....140
The fight is on.....132
There's danger in...328
We're fighting 169
Yield not to.......327

Trust

All of my need.... 8
All the way 97
Be not dismayed .. 37
Christ will me 25
Does the world ... 16
Faith of our.......150
High as the....... 72
If you need 76
In the shadow..... 84
I've found a Friend.. 4
Jesus is all 5
Jesus Lover of 225
Just when I need... 22
Long by sin.......106
My faith looks 233
My hope is........275
My Shepherd is....141
Nothing satisfies .. 83
Sweet are the..... 90
There's one who ... 7
'Tis so sweet......109
'Tis sweet to know. 78
When I have...... 82
When peace like... 12

Warfare

(See Conflict)

Worship

Abide with me......266
All hail the power..249
All the way........ 97
All people that 340
Come Thou Almighty.229
Come Thou Fount..238
Crown Him with ... 11
Day is dying...... 40
Fade, fade each....251
From Greenland's ..253
Guide me O Thou..262
Holy, holy, holy....258
How firm a.......223
I love Thy.........244
I would give Thee.. 99
Jesus Friend of.... 3
Jesus I my cross...267
Jesus keep me 127
Jesus Lover 225
Jesus the very.....246
Love divine all 270
Majestic sweetness .256
More love to Thee..133
My faith looks 233
My Jesus I love....241
Nearer my God....239
Nearer the cross ...274
Nearer still nearer ..125
O how precious ... 34
O listen to our.....115
O sacred Head 257
O worship the King.260
Oh for a 252
Rock of Ages 273
Savior more than ..157
Savior Thy dying.. 129
Sweet hour of 276
'Tis the blessed.... 9
What a Friend 261